ADDI

What they
happen - ... help

by

LIZ HODGKINSON

THORSONS PUBLISHING GROUP
Wellingborough · New York

First published 1986

© LIZ HODGKINSON 1986

British Library Cataloguing in Publication Data

Hodgkinson, Liz
　　Addictions: what they are — why they
happen — how to help.
　　1. Alcoholism　　2. Drug abuses
　　I. Title
　　362.2'9　　　HV5035

ISBN 0-7225-1246-5

Printed and bound in Great Britain

CONTENTS

INTRODUCTION

If we were all perfectly happy, perfectly content and felt peaceful all the time, we would very probably not have the slightest desire to drink alcohol, smoke, gamble, or take any drugs.

But few people go through life like this, without any artificial props whatever. Indeed, hardly anyone would want to, as an existence deprived of sensation, excitement and temptation would, for most of us, be dull indeed. The trouble is that many of the so-called 'good' things in life, such as wine, cigars, fast driving, and gambling for high stakes, can have a nasty habit of taking hold and taking over. When this happens, when we feel that we can't live without an hourly puff on a cigarette, or a regular tot of whisky, we are in danger of becoming addicted to the object that is capable of providing the exhilaration, stimulation or relaxation. In time, life may actually become unbearable without a regular dose of the mind-altering substance or activity.

Many teenagers lightheartedly have a go at smoking cigarettes and usually the first few puffs cause coughs, splutters, and a definite feeling of nausea. But after a very short time these unpleasant reactions usually vanish and, once the system has got used to receiving regular amounts of smoke, definite benefits are experienced. Then, almost before the teenager realizes what is happening, he or she is hooked, and it becomes painful to go for more than a few hours without lighting up.

The same can happen with alcohol which, after you have become used to it, can impart a marvellously sedative and relaxing effect. Sweet foods, similarly, can make you feel calm and at peace with the world, blotting out niggling anxieties — at least for a short time. Gambling and fast driving are of the opposite kind of addiction — they speed up the flow of adrenalin, the hormone that can make you feel glad to be alive.

There are basically two kinds of substances or activities that can result in addictions developing: those that stimulate, and those that have a relaxing effect. But whatever the object or substance that provides the longed-for satisfaction, the end result is much the same. After a time the body begins to crave and actually to demand physically the alien substance that, for so many years, it managed perfectly well without. When this happens, we can say that a person is addicted. Certain drugs, such as cannabis and LSD, are often referred to as 'non-addictive'. This means that, although considerable psychological lifts may be obtained from indulging in them, they do not cause physical dependency, and acute withdrawal symptoms will not result if the stuff is suddenly withheld for any reason.

The human body is infinitely adaptable and can in time even alter its cell structure to accommodate a physically addictive drug. In some cases, the body will literally come to depend on the chemical for its daily functioning and will complain in no uncertain way when the substance is denied it. In fact, with some drugs, you may become extremely ill if they are withdrawn. This is what many people taking tranquillizers have found to their cost. When they tried to stop taking the drugs, acute mental and physical symptoms set in.

However, although most people, in the Western world at least, will at some stage in their lives try out smoking, drinking and, increasingly, mind-altering drugs, by no means everybody will become addicted to them. Many teenagers who try an occasional cigarette or cannabis joint will never develop a taste for either, while others may be hooked almost from the first drag. There is a very big difference between enjoying an occasional drink and being alcohol-dependent, between having a modest flutter and haunting casinos night after night. Why is it that so many people are able to indulge only occasionally, while others are completely dependent on their habit?

What is addictive behaviour and why does it set in in some people? And why do so many people seem to be succumbing to addictive habits? There is little doubt that the number of addicts, whether their downfall is gambling, drinking or drugs, is increasing all the time. The only addictive substance that does seem to be decreasing in popularity is tobacco, yet still over one-third of the nation's adults are smokers.

This book cannot claim to have all the answers, but it sets out to try to come to terms with the nature of various addictions, and explain how and why they can take hold. Whenever a person is caught in the grip of an addiction, it is extremely worrying for family, friends and colleagues. It often seems as though the addict is hell-bent on personal destruction and that there is little the onlooker can do to help.

For both the addict and the family, any serious addiction represents a grave life crisis that often needs extremely skilled help and understanding from all involved. This book is written both for addicts and those around them, so that each can understand the problem more fully and be helped to reverse the downward spiral of behaviour and health that characterizes drug or alcohol dependency or, indeed, any addiction.

However deeply ingrained the habit may have become, no one should give up all hope. Addictions can always be conquered, given the will to overcome them. Some people who are ignorant of the issues involved tend to despise and reject addicts. These people feel that addictions are self-inflicted problems and that those who are dependent deserve all they get. But anyone in the grip of an uncontrollable addiction is suffering from an illness just as surely as if they were victims of heart disease or cancer, and an addict can no longer be considered as someone outside decent society: he or she could be a friend, a neighbour, your own parent, partner or child — or even yourself.

PART ONE

1.

WHAT ARE ADDICTIONS?

Who Becomes an Addict?

It is true that most of the people who have a go at gambling, or who taste alcohol, will never become so hooked that their very health and sanity is threatened by their dependency. But the truth is also that anyone can become an addict. Addictions can, and do, affect people from all social classes, of all degrees of intelligence, and at all professional levels. Today, a heroin addict is just as likely to come from the upper echelons of the aristocracy as from a slum tenement. An alcoholic may be a highly-qualified professional person or an unemployable mental defective. One of the saddest cases of alcoholism I have encountered was in a man who had been the headmaster of a large comprehensive school. Through his addiction, he eventually became a homeless tramp. In fact, many of the tramps that one sees shuffling about the streets were once quite respectable men.

About eighteen million prescriptions are written out every year in this country for tranquillizers. Those who take them may be housewives who cannot cope with a seemingly meaningless existence and who have difficulty in dusting their homes, or high-flying career women who appear to have everything going for them; or they may be men having some trouble at work. A gambling addict may be someone who gets through several thousand pounds a night in Mayfair casinos, or an old lady who uses nearly all of her pension money to go to bingo. Where an addiction is concerned, there is no difference between the man who tries to double his dole money, and the smooth chap in the grey topper and tails who puts large sums on horses at the Royal Enclosure at Ascot.

In its simplest terms, an addiction sets in when, somewhere along the line, we start to like a particular activity more than we would usually. At least, we begin to like the effect it gives us. In an attempt to sustain that feeling of well-being, we keep taking in the substance, or pursuing the activity. Before long we have learned to enjoy greatly, or come to depend on, the state of mind that results. Then, sooner or later, without us noticing, we find we actually can't do without it.

Most smokers don't actually like smoking very much: they hate spending money on cigarettes, hate the smell, and dislike their ashtrays being continuously full of ends. They also hate the dependency that makes them terrified of running out of cigarettes. However, the pleasures derived whilst actually inhaling are strong enough to overcome all these unaesthetic and unwelcome aspects. Smoking is hard to give up because nicotine has both a sedative and a stimulating effect on the brain. And this effect is not just psychological — it is physical as well.

As we continue to smoke, drink or take drugs, the habit may become ever more deeply ingrained so that, in the end, it actually becomes a part of us and an aspect of our personality. One reason why smokers can find attempts to relinquish their habit so painful is that, after a time, nicotine actually becomes part of their chemical make-up and enters every cell in the body, altering its chemical construction. The same can happen with a drug like heroin. This, too, significantly alters the body's chemical components and workings, and it becomes an integral part of the system. Heroin is particularly pernicious because it replaces the body's natural painkillers. When people take heroin, production of these natural painkillers stops and this is the main reason for the agony of withdrawal. If the supply of heroin stops abruptly then neither the artificial painkiller nor the natural painkiller is present in the body.

Although heroin has a particularly dramatic effect on the body in this way, all addictions work in a similar fashion. The human body adapts itself so that, in the end, it cannot work properly without the alien substance. This is really why addicts return again and again to their fix. After a fairly short time actual active enjoyment in the substance lessens, but addicts continue taking the stuff because they dread withdrawal symptoms.

Addictions of any kind can become so ingrained that removing them is rather like tearing off a limb. In time, they are not simply a support, an adjunct, like a walking stick or a hearing aid, but become part of the body itself, central to daily existence. That is the real danger of allowing addictive substances and addictive forms of behaviour to take hold. They become part of you, and then you can no longer choose not to use them.

One of the big problems facing those who try to help addicts is that, if they are not addicted themselves, they can find it hard to understand both the pleasures and the pains associated with the dependency. Addictive behaviour does not usually seem sensible to the onlooker and it can be tempting just to turn one's back on those under the influence. But however bad an addiction may be for family and friends to observe, it is always far worse for the addict.

The reason why addicts do not just give up their addictions is because they truly believe they can't. Rationally, a gambler may know that to be dependent on the turn of a roulette wheel, or the outcome of a horse race, is ridiculous. It can ruin his life, and turn him into a criminal, a liar and a cheat. Rationally, also, a heroin addict knows as well as anybody else that the chemical is bringing about absolute devastation in her life. But this knowledge and understanding is never as strong as the emotional drive, or the physical dependency. An addict is continually compelled to seek out the substance or activity because he cannot help it. He is no longer in charge of his life, or what he does. The addiction has taken over.

Somehow, an addict will always get hold of the money to gamble, drink or take drugs, even if he has to steal to do it. Addictions drive people to desperate behaviour, that can be hard for outsiders to comprehend. Sooner or later, a compulsive gambler will be involved with crime and many end up in prison. In fact, a significant proportion of all those behind bars are there because of a gambling habit. Heroin, which is illegal to start with, brings addicts very quickly into contact with criminals. In some ways, this very image of the 'outsider' can be one of the less obvious but seductive attractions of the addiction. Any form of compulsive behaviour will, sooner or later, put the addict outside society.

An addiction is also very expensive. A compulsive gambler is defined by Gamblers Anonymous as somebody who is spending more than they can afford on the habit. Though heroin is now relatively cheap to buy, and a fix can be bought for as little as £5 for a new addict, in time the habit will cost hundreds of pounds a week. As most addicts soon lose their jobs, where are they to find this kind of money? Usually only by resorting to crime.

The Choice of 'Poison'

What predisposes a person to choose a particular substance? Why do some people like to gamble and smoke, while others become hooked on heroin or cocaine? Why do some people take tranquillizers, while others will wildly overeat?

Although many addicts are multiple abusers, in that they will smoke, drink, take heroin and cocaine and gamble, all at the same time, not all addicts are addicted to everything. In the end, a person's choice of 'poison' — the addictive substance that has the power to impart the desired mind-altering state — comes down to a matter of personality, opportunity, availability, finance, social custom and lifestyle. Heroin addiction was unknown two hundred years ago because the substance didn't then exist. Similarly nobody was addicted to tranquillizers in the 1930s, because they hadn't then been formulated. In Victorian times, people were addicted to laudanum, opium and chloroform. Substances and activities change according to fashion and to what is available.

It is possible to become addicted to a far wider range of activities than many people realize. Though heroin and alcohol abuse are much in the news, there are those who are equally addicted to romantic novels, knitting, computers, or bird watching. Not all addictions are equally dangerous, but no kind of obsession can be considered a good thing.

There are certain important sex differences in addictions. Far more men than women are compulsive gamblers and drinkers, although the instances of females succumbing to both is rising rapidly. This is partly because, in the past at least, men had greater opportunity to gamble and drink and be outside the house. More women are now turning to these because, in some ways, women now have lifestyles, stresses and anxieties which in the past were traditionally male. Addictions always take hold when a person is under great stress — a non-stressed individual, whatever their sex, will never become addicted. The dependency serves to blot out the perception of some deeply-felt pain and the choice of substance often comes down to what may be near at hand when a prop is needed. Cigarettes and alcohol are easily available, and both are legal, so many people will turn to these. Heroin is more difficult to obtain, and illegal, therefore it is still slightly rarer.

But addictions do not develop just because the substance is there. Anybody who has a deep-seated need to blot out some inner anguish will find something that does the trick. Poverty-stricken youngsters may turn to solvents, which are cheap and easily available; the non-earning housewife may go to her doctor for pills which can be prescribed for next to nothing; and high-earning film stars may sniff expensive cocaine.

Far more women than men become hooked on tranquillizers and sleeping pills. This happens for a number of reasons. One is that women go to their doctors more than men anyway, and it has been shown in various studies that male doctors are likely to give calming pills to their female patients. The other main reason is that tranquillizers are a passive, non-assertive way of dealing with pain and dissatisfaction. A man is more liable to be angry at his frustration with life, and also to find his own way of coping, rather than relying on a doctor.

More males than females become heroin addicts, and by far the great majority of female addicts are introduced to the habit by their boyfriends, or some other older male who is already using heroin. As a very, very broad generalization, capable of many exceptions, it seems that men are more likely to choose outgoing, aggressive, extrovert activities, and women more liable to go for the passive, secretive types of addiction. It is women, rather than men, who overeat wildly, who are addicted to sweet things, to romantic novels, soap operas, or even to compulsive tidiness and cleanliness. Women tend to choose addictions that are less obvious, and which nobody need know about.

Men are more liable to become workaholics and speed freaks, while women may become 'clothesaholics'. Overspenders Anonymous, which is for people who can't stop themselves shopping for clothes and other items that they do not need and will never use, has a large female membership in America. Men may turn into computer addicts — it is rare to come across women who are unable to tear themselves away from high-tech machines — while women may become obsessive knitters or embroiderers.

There is always a distinct danger that any addiction, even an addiction to work and productivity, will take over your life in such a way that eventually there is no room left for anything else.

When is a Person Addicted?

Usually, we can say that an addiction has well and truly set in when the chemical balance of the body has become significantly altered as a result, and when the addictive substance has become an individual's best, and indeed only, friend. All addictions affect body processes. Sugar addiction affects the blood; tobacco affects the brain; and alcohol and heroin depress the central nervous system, to bring about, in the short term at least, a feeling of relaxation and peace. Drugs such as cocaine and amphetamine have the opposite effect, as they speed up bodily reactions and stimulate the central nervous system to bring about a feeling of exhilaration and excitement.

Gambling and fast driving send continual rushes of adrenalin through the system. Even certain types of behaviour, such as being addicted to anger or depression, can keep the body's delicate chemical balance subtly altered. Although the body may have welcomed the altered balance at first, and later come to depend on it, in time the system starts to rebel and serious illness can be the result. A long-term addiction constitutes a serious assault on bodily functions and can eventually lead to the complete breakdown of internal organs.

One question often asked is: if you are addicted to a mind-altering substance or activity, which is the 'real' you? Are we seeing the real person when he is drunk, or when he is sober? The popular saying *in vino veritas* implies that through drink the true person is revealed. But the drink-abuse charity ACCEPT, which now helps with other addictions as well, is in no doubt as to the answer. The real, genuine person is the sober, non-addicted one. Drink, or drugs, bring out only a false person. Addicts themselves may feel that they are nicer, more humane, loving or caring people when under the influence, but that is rarely the impression that others gain.

Addicts tend to be people who cannot seem to achieve the state of mind and personality that they desire by ordinary means, so they adopt an artificial solution. Alcohol can, in the very short term, make people appear to be more witty, outgoing and extrovert. But this effect doesn't last and it soon turns into intoxication, which is not attractive. It is a fact that a person's character can never be altered for the better by the pursuance of mind-altering substances. But it can, very definitely, be changed for the worse — and that is the true perniciousness of addictive substances. Eventually, they wreck the personality and bring about self-hate, lack of self-respect, and can completely destroy a person's confidence.

Addictions are so very powerful that most people who have been caught in their grip but manage to set themselves free feel that, once the link with the dreaded substance has been broken, life must in future be lived without even the merest taste of it again. Thus, compulsive gamblers who attend Gamblers

Anonymous meetings are told they must never even buy a Premium Bond as the habit, once it has taken hold, may come out again. Once an addict, always an addict, they believe.

The various 'Anonymous' organizations, all of which originated in the United States, believe that addictions never go away and cannot be cured. They can, however, be permanently controlled, although former addicts will tend to tread on a knife edge all their lives. Former alcoholics must not even have one tiny drop of shandy, or celebrate a wedding with an alcoholic drink. Ex-smokers must not take the merest puff again, otherwise the body, which became so used to a regular intake, could remember the sensation and crave it again. Most help agencies for heroin addiction believe that there is no way to enjoy an occasional sniff or snort. If you come off the drug, you come off it completely and must never touch it again.

Narcotics Anonymous, the self-help association for drug addicts, go even further. They believe a former addict must, in future, succumb to no mind-altering substances whatever. There is little point, they say, in simply replacing one addiction with another.

A classic and tragic example of this kind is the story of the late Jim Fixx. He took up jogging when he was a shambling, overweight, stress-prone businessman. The compulsive eating, drinking and working stopped, but he became so addicted to running that in the end it killed him at the early age of fifty-two. He ran to gain that sought-after 'runner's high', that surge of adrenalin which courses through the veins during strenuous sport.

Jogging may seem less harmful than uncontrolled drinking or gambling, but the addictive aspect can become just as pernicious. With running, the 'high' lasts only for a short time and then you have to run again to bring back the feeling of well-being. After a period, you may want to experience that 'high' all the time and not have the 'low' that inevitably accompanies it. This is true of all addicts — they want the pleasures, but can't bear the pains of withdrawal. This is what sends addicts in search of ever higher doses of their fix, so that the pain will never return.

The Pleasure of Addictions

Nobody would become addicted to anything if they had not, at some stage, derived considerable benefits and pleasure from the substance. At first heroin conveys a feeling of deep peace, which the addict then wants to experience endlessly. The main pleasure to be derived from an addictive substance is that it has the power to convey instant satisfaction. There is no waiting.

If you go on a slimming diet, or a course of study, it may be many months before results start to show. There is no instant reward for eating less — you don't become sylph-like in a day. Similarly, if you are learning a new language, you don't become fluent overnight. But with a cigarette, an alcoholic drink, or a narcotic, you gain the results at once. Those who inject or snort heroin receive its sensations literally seconds later. Most drinkers, on entering a pub, order their favourite tipple and down it in an instant saying, 'That's better.'

All the substances that can cause addictions have become multi-million pound industries, the illegal as well as the legal ones, for this very reason: they deliver satisfaction at once. Addictions are, for those dealing in substances which cause dependency, very big business indeed. And for many of the addictive substances, except perhaps for heroin, there is undoubtedly a glamorous, desirable side. Racehorses are sleek, beautiful animals, worth many thousands of pounds; cigars and cigarettes come attractively packaged; and there is certainly much pleasure in choosing and drinking fine wines. Yet all these are potentially addictive, and can cause serious dependency problems.

The main problem is that a significant and growing proportion of people are unable, for a variety of reasons, to keep their pleasures, and the indulgence in these substances, occasional. There is always the danger with any of them that they may take over a person's life, eventually destroying it.

The Pain of Addictions
Pain from addictions results when the craving has become so deeply embedded that there is both physical and psychological dependency. In some severe cases the body cannot function any more without a regular supply of the addictive substance. Then life becomes one long agony, relieved only when the substance enters the body. But apart from deeply affecting health, always to its detriment, addictions have an adverse effect on an individual's personality as well.

The addict — whatever the cause of the addiction — can come to suffer from very severe personality defects once the addiction has taken hold. Self-respect, self-esteem and self-confidence are lost as addicts begin to feel they are nothing, that they do not exist, without their fix. The classic path for addicts is that, somewhere along the line, they start to hate themselves, and they become hideously tormented by the hold their addiction has gained. After a time most addicts truly do want to kick the habit that has enslaved them but, by this time, they can't. They can no longer exercise free will in the matter. Both their minds and their bodies have come to depend on the substance for daily functioning.

An addiction can be so very powerful that it can actually turn someone into a quite different, and not very likeable, person. Whereas before an individual may have been intelligent, witty, or wise, once in the grip of a dependency, this same person will be hostile, resentful, secretive, self-pitying: in short, they display all the least attractive negative qualities.

The only way to regain one's former personality is by learning to break the hold of the addiction. In fact, all addicts eventually become just like one another. Nearly all mood-altering chemicals, whether found in drink or drugs, or manufactured internally as the result of gambling, bring about the same end result in those dependent on them. Whatever individual personality characteristics a person may have possessed at one time, these become lost as the addiction takes an ever-stronger hold.

Most addicts end up as self-loathers. Whereas previously they may have disliked some aspect of themselves, and sought to overcome this by taking in a chemical, once they are completely under the influence, they become a seething mass of hatred against themselves. This is why so many addicts attempt, and many succeed, in committing suicide.

Overcoming Addictions
As addictions seem to have become more common, many agencies have grown up to help people rid themselves of their dependency. These vary from self-help organizations to doctors, social workers, psychiatrists and other professionals. All fight an uphill battle, as the difficulty is to persuade the addict, or for the addict to persuade himself, that there is a better life out there without the artificial substance.

The groups that have become most successful in helping people overcome their addictions are those that manage to stress the positive aspects. Instead of trying to encourage people simply to give up, they work on helping them to develop strategies for living that will be more rewarding. It is certainly not easy, as any addict comes to rely on his fix to help him cope with life and whenever a crisis looms he will be tempted to fall back on the easy solution — the fix. It has solved many problems before. The patterns of behaviour will have become very deeply ingrained.

All successful drink- and drug-abuse agencies understand that nature abhors a vacuum, and that any addiction will be taking up a lot of the addict's time and thought. You cannot just remove it, leaving nothing in its place. It also has to be understood, from the outset, that no addiction can ever be overcome *unless the addict actually wants to change*. Families and friends cannot themselves provide the motivation, although they can be very instrumental in giving the correct type of support at the right time. But no amount of threats, promises or bribes will make the slightest difference to anybody who does not really want to give up their addiction.

It is true that no addiction can be controlled unless the addict comes to possess the unshakeable conviction that life can be immeasurably improved without the dependency. This is a far from simple matter. Many heroin addicts, for instance, go for detoxification cures and come out of their rehabilitation homes supposedly freed of the habit. But when they get once more into the outside world, with all its challenges, they may find it a cold, hostile and unfriendly place. Maybe they cannot find work, perhaps they are unable to form proper relationships with other people. They can then imagine that life on heroin isn't so bad after all — at least it blots out the miseries of the real world, and saves people from having to make difficult decisions about how to conduct their lives. In a very short time ex-addicts can be using heroin again, and many are.

Most experts who work with addicts feel that, once someone has been addicted, there is always the possibility that the desire to drink, take drugs or gamble, will return. It is easy to keep the habit under control for a short time, but if motivation weakens it may well return.

Constant vigilance is required, not least by the addict. It is usually necessary to break off all former links with the previous life, establish a new set of friends and move to a different neighbourhood. Anything that serves to remind a former user of his dependency must be stringently avoided. For some ex-gamblers, watching horseracing on television would be enough to set the old desires in motion again. Though physical dependency can be reversed fairly quickly, even with drugs such as heroin, it is a far more difficult matter to replace the psychological addiction, the personality problem that enabled the addiction to take hold in the first place.

It is difficult for non-addicts to see the attraction and to understand how anyone could let an artificial chemical or any activity have such a hold on their life. A non-addicted person may see a man so hooked on alcohol that he has lost his home, job, family and friends. He has lost everything, but still he continues to drink. Why, the non-addict may wonder, can't he kick the habit? Can't he see what it is doing to him? Can't he see that it is killing him?

The addict cannot 'see sense' because, by this time, his brain has become so deeply affected by the drink (or whatever) that it is simply not working in the same way as that of a non-addicted person. It has become a fog, through which he can no longer see clearly the results of his actions. All he eventually understands is that, somehow, he must stumble towards another drink. Gamblers are exactly the same in this respect: the processes by which others think and act have become lost to them because of their addiction.

This is why the road back can be so long and painful, and even impossible if, deep down, the addict does not want to break the habit and take his or her place back in the world of reality.

Those helping addicts, or who live with them, must realize that any habit, if pursued with enough dedication, and over a long enough period of time, can eventually be a potent way of permanently altering the consciousness. An addiction is a way of coping with problems. It is not a very satisfactory way, perhaps, but it is a solution of a kind. Life becomes very simple for an addict, as his whole life is concerned only to obtain more of the fix. The habit cannot be overcome until more rewarding solutions can be discovered.

All the 'Anonymous' organizations are self-help groups in that they are run by former users of the substance, rather than by doctors or other professionals. The idea is that former addicts are the best people to understand other addicts, but it is also true that helping others in itself constitutes excellent therapy. Anybody who is trying to overcome an addiction must be helped to lead a life which they will consider useful and satisfying. To a former addict, there is often no activity more rewarding than helping others who remain hooked. It must be said, however, that the self-help approach does not work for everybody. There are those who are not, or who do not become, strong enough to help themselves, and these are the ones who need expert, professional care.

Unfortunately, there are not enough help agencies to sort out the problems of all those addicted. As with all bad habits it is easy enough to develop an addiction, but less easy to reverse it. Most charitable agencies are underfunded, constantly short of staff, and have more clients than they can really handle. All the main ways of overcoming addictions will be described in detail in this book. The answer is to find the one that best suits the individual.

Those who live with an addict have to bear in mind that their own behaviour can either help or hinder. Many parents of heroin addicts, for example, may make their children's habit worse simply by not understanding the problem, or by taking the attitude of: how could you do this to me?

Many wives of alcoholic husbands actually do drive their husbands to drink by their own disapproving and negative behaviour. Those involved with an addict have to know that they cannot hope to change the addict's behaviour: they can only alter their own. If they improve, then the user may start to improve as well. This is a very hard lesson to learn, and it seems very unfair, but certain help agencies, such as ACCEPT and Families Anonymous, for the relatives of drug addicts, now concentrate on helping relatives to come to terms with their own attitudes first, as a preliminary step to aiding the addict.

Many have found that this, in itself, can trigger off a welcome upward spiral. The very worst thing that any relative of an addict can do is to 'write off' the unfortunate person, implying or telling them outright that they are no good and not worth helping. This will only serve to drive the addict further into gloom and despair, and will deepen the dependency.

However bad the addiction may be, it is always possible to free oneself from it, so long as the conditions, the motivation, and the right sort of help, are there.

PART TWO

2.

DRUGS

Introduction

Over the past few years there have been a steadily increasing number of stories, both in the press and on television, about heroin abuse. In 1985 the Department of Health and Social Security began a large-scale campaign, endorsed by many rock stars, to try and avert this fast-growing menace, which is claiming ever more vulnerable young people among its victims.

As the drug remains illegal, except for very restricted medical use, it is not possible to obtain accurate figures for heroin dependence, but conservative estimates now put the current number of users in the UK at over 10,000. According to Pete Townshend, former member of the rock group The Who, and himself a one-time heroin addict, the total number of people dependent on this drug could be as high as two million — in Britain alone.

Heroin is definitely the young people's scourge of the 1980s. Almost every day we hear about it, and now virtually everyone knows somebody whose son or daughter is addicted, or who has at least come into contact with the stuff. We are now used to opening up our morning papers and seeing the gaunt face, staring eyes and emaciated frame of yet another user. These sad individuals come, it appears, from every class of society, from the most privileged and wealthy backgrounds to the most deprived slum homes.

But even though there are now so many stories about heroin abuse, and so many articles have appeared on junkies and the pushers, the subject is still shrouded in mystery. What exactly is heroin? Why is it so feared? And who are these evil 'pushers' about which one hears so much?

If you stopped one hundred people in the street and asked

them these questions, you would be lucky to find one who could give the answers with any accuracy. Most people understand that heroin comes from the opium poppy and originates from China. Nearly everybody imagines that all you need is one shot to be hopelessly hooked for life. The subject undoubtedly holds a lurid fascination and contains all the ingredients of a murky thriller. Big-time crime is involved, we understand, and the Mafia, Chinese Triads and so on. En route, many thousands of lives are wrecked by the stuff.

Not so long ago, heroin was for most of us a rather unreal, fantasy substance. We may have heard of it, but it did not touch, even remotely, our everyday lives. Now, it is not so far removed from suburban existence and can actually be bought quite easily and openly in virtually every town. This factor has in itself given rise to another potent myth about heroin: that on almost every street corner nowadays a pusher lies in wait, ready to trap another unsuspecting youngster into a web of addiction, vice and crime.

The fact is that by far the vast majority of users obtain their first fix from friends and acquaintances, and most are introduced to the substance by their own circle of friends. It is virtually unknown to be initiated into the habit by a stranger. Further, there is no doubt that heroin embraces a criminal world from start to finish, and also no doubt that this extremely addictive substance is becoming ever more widely used. But it is not possible to justify the view that the substance is instantly enslaving, agony to withdraw from, and that one shot turns once upright citizens and healthy boys and girls into burnt-out junkies.

Although there is very little one can say in favour of heroin, it should be realized at the outset that it is not an automatic slippery slope, and that many who try heroin once do not feel the need to take it again. Also, the majority of adolescents will never even try the stuff. But against this we should not be complacent: the drug does have a very high addiction potential, and young people should be vigorously dissuaded from ever thinking it is glamorous and trying it out.

Unless it is understood exactly what heroin is, and how it affects the mind and body, parents and concerned onlookers can be of very little help to the teenager who might be wavering. Ignorance among non-drug-taking adults is particularly despised by young people, who will take no notice of dire warnings unless these are based on clear understanding and the knowledge that casts out fear.

Heroin is definitely the major mind-altering drug of the moment. It is not the most widely used: far more people drink alcohol and take cannabis than have ever tried sniffing or snorting heroin. The difference is that, while ninety per cent of those who drink wine or use cannabis occasionally will not be addicted, ninety per cent of those who use heroin *will* become hooked. In fact, one might almost say that people take heroin with the intention of becoming hooked on it, using it as an anaesthetic rather than to be sociable. Since the 1960s there have been several scary drugs around. First of all it was purple hearts — actually blue triangles — and during the 1970s barbiturates were the main misused drug. These two manufactured drugs, while still being used and abused, feature far less nowadays, and have gone right out of fashion.

Today's parents of teenagers are men and women who were themselves young in the 1960s and who were probably the first generation to experiment with cannabis or its derivatives, marijuana and hashish. In those days, cannabis was often taken at parties to heighten awareness and perception, mainly by university students. Heroin was virtually unknown, at least in Britain. It was associated with the dark side of American culture and even then had an evil reputation.

In those days, heroin was difficult to obtain and very expensive. But now it is not even so costly. For new users, an effective fix can be bought for as little as £5. Tolerance soon develops, however, and it can soon cost £300 or more a week (in 1985) to support a full-blown heroin habit.

It is vital that anybody who wishes to understand the drug scene today should know the difference between the various substances that can cause mental and physical changes in users. Psychoactive drugs in use vary very greatly in their effects and by no means all are physically addictive. Cannabis and LSD, for example, while possibly promoting psychological dependence if used regularly, and certainly not to be recommended in any way, are not physically addictive. This means that they do not affect every cell in the body and alter its chemical composition. Physical addiction means that, in time, the body actually cannot function without the once-alien chemical and comes to rely on it. The human body is almost infinitely adaptable and can learn to accommodate many poisonous and deadly substances. This is what happens with heroin: it affects both brain and body cells in a very intimate way, and alters the workings of every cell in the body — that is why people become dependent on it.

Chemically-active drugs act either as stimulants or depressants. Solvents, heroin and barbiturates have an effect rather like alcohol in that they depress the central nervous system to bring about a feeling of calm, well-being, and relaxation. Other drugs, notably cocaine and amphetamines, are stimulants and arouse all body systems, including the brain. This is why the amphetamines are called 'speed' — they speed up body functions and make users feel more alert and alive.

The most worrying questions for today's parents are whether their children will turn to drugs, and how they can prevent it happening. If they cannot actually prevent drugs being used, they want to know what the best ways are of helping youngsters to come off them. Although there is no absolute guarantee that loving care, concern and calm knowledge will do the trick, there is definitely much that parents can do to minimize the risk. One of these is to discover the exact actions of the drugs used today, rather than lumping them all together under the same heading.

It is an understatement to say that it is not nice to have an addict in the family. It has been estimated that an addict, on average, disrupts the lives of five other people, and most of these will be close relatives. Parents usually feel a mixture of guilt, rage, upset, shock and disbelief when they learn that their child has become a drug user. A common reaction is: how could you do this to me? The most difficult task of all is to learn to have the right attitude towards the user: a too-condemnatory or too-sympathetic approach may each serve to drive the habit home even harder.

A very hard lesson for parents to learn is that they must act as detached observers, and help their children without becoming too involved. No users will ever come off drugs to please a parent, nor will they ever kick the habit until they are ready. Nobody else can provide the motivation or determination. If parents issue dire warnings against all drugs, and bombard their children with scare stories, this may have absolutely the opposite effect to the one intended. They may succeed only in making the drug sound glamorous and the mark of a rebel; and almost all teenagers want to rebel against their parents at some time. Adults are often horrified when they learn that their teenage children have experimented with cannabis. Although in fact, these days, it is a rare adolescent who has *not* taken cannabis at some stage.

I once asked a fifteen-year-old whether he had ever taken cannabis. 'Of course,' he said without surprise. 'Where did you get it from?' I persisted. 'The Portobello Road,' he answered. Then he explained the circumstances. 'There were three of us who bought it together. It wasn't hard to find. Then we took it to a quiet place, the most peaceful and beautiful spot we could find, out in the country. We did the whole thing properly, and rolled up a joint which we handed round and smoked to Simon and Garfunkel music.'

Was there any effect? 'Oh yes, we all felt different. There was definitely a high, and it was a nice feeling. But we decided we wouldn't take it again. We've experimented, we know what it's like, and that's enough.'

'Would you try heroin?'

'No way. I want to stay healthy, and I've got no intention of becoming addicted to a drug. Heroin's for mugs.'

'Do you know what heroin is?'

'Oh yes, it comes from opium, and it's made from morphine. It's very addictive, and it makes you sick when you withdraw, like getting bad flu.'

This clued-up teenager is, I suggest, typical of many young people of today. He knew far more about drugs than his parents, and had a far more sensible attitude. Just about all secondary schools these days have a 'drug problem' in that cannabis is widely taken. Daphne Rae, wife of the former headmaster of Westminster School, said in her book, *A World Apart* (Lutterworth Press, 1983), that any school which denied there was drug-taking was simply pulling the wool over its eyes. Cannabis is available at just about every school, and is on offer at most parties. But cannabis is not heroin, and is very different from it.

If parents discover that their children have been taking cannabis, the very worst thing they can do is to pitch in with a diatribe against the evils of drug-taking. Any child who has taken cannabis occasionally without experiencing any harmful side-effects will conclude that the parent knows nothing, is merely a killjoy and a fuddy-duddy, and will not then believe the parents when they inveigh against heroin. Research undertaken by the DHSS revealed that scare stories and detailed films about drug abuse merely underlined the appeal of heroin, rather than working to persuade anybody against it.

A wise parent will be on the watch, without giving any indication that there is worry or concern. It is rare that a person in the early stages of serious drug-taking will inform the parent of their habit and, as the early warning signs may be similar to adolescent mood swings and bodily upsets generally, they can easily be missed. This is especially the case if, as so often happens, the child is living away from home.

This section of the book concentrates mainly on heroin, its use and abuse, as this is by far the most worrying illegal drug of today. But, in order to put it all into perspective, all the other main illegal drugs and their actions are also outlined.

Heroin

The background

Heroin is definitely the in drug at the moment and it has, to some extent, caused the other illegal drugs to pale into temporary insignificance. It is an opiate, and belongs to the same family of drugs as morphine, codeine, diconal and methadone.

The word 'heroin' was coined in 1898 by Heinrich Dreser, who was at the time chief pharmacist of the pharmaceutical company Friedrich Bayer and Son. The stuff was first used as a cough mixture and was actually discovered in 1878, seventy years after morphine was isolated from opium. Dreser alleged that heroin was not habit-forming and foresaw it becoming a useful medicine. We have Herr Dreser to thank, incidentally, for naming another drug which has become a household name — aspirin.

From the start, heroin and the other opium derivatives were used as painkillers, and are still considered useful drugs, for certain terminal illnesses. The drug remained almost entirely in medical use until the 1950s, when the first heroin addicts — those who were using the drug for non-medical reasons — were notified to the Home Office. In 1950, there were about twenty-five of these, and they were all jazz musicians who had picked up the habit while abroad.

Since then, its non-medical use has grown and grown. In fact, nowadays, more people use heroin non-therapeutically than for medicinal reasons. The newspapers are full of horror stories about the growing heroin epidemic and the British government is seriously worried about how best to stamp it out. Daily, heroin appears to draw more people into its grip: around 10,000 new addicts are now notified to the Home Office each year, and many, many more are never notified.

The users

The heroin drug, which once had working-class associations, now knows no class boundaries; but there do appear to be age limits. It is rare for users to be over thirty years old, and the habit usually starts at around the age of eighteen.

The word heroin, which was coined so innocently, now has the power to evoke a powerful combination of emotions and images: there is fear and terror, mixed with dark fascination, as we conjure up pictures of evil Chinese triads, and illicit lorryloads being smuggled from Pakistani borders. The photograph of a burnt-out junkie injecting into his arm has become a newspaper cliché. Indeed most newspapers have, readily prepared, such a picture to illustrate any heroin story or investigation. Over the past five years heroin has become the most talked about, the most feared, and the most investigated drug in recent history.

Heroin pushers have been described as the world's most highly motivated sales force, and its employees are all professional criminals. At one time, Britain was merely a transit point for the heroin trade, but now there is a thriving black market, with over £100 million worth of trade being executed annually. In fact, many people believe that Britain is now becoming the drug centre of the world. In 1983, according to investigator Brian Freemantle, heroin seizures in this country of £45 million were an all-time record. Heroin can be bought easily in any British town, for as little as £5 a bag. Its use is so fast growing that in 1983 eighty-five per cent of all first notifications were for heroin.

As all heroin pushers are in it for the money, and as the drug continues to be illegal, purity of supplies cannot be guaranteed, and this is one of the murky complications of heroin. Addicts are always at the mercy of those who may be adulterating or 'cutting' supplies with other white powders that look similar. This is really where the biggest danger lies. Most experts are of the opinion that in small, pure doses, heroin does little harm, but when it is mixed with other substances, as it usually is in street supplies, it can quickly destroy body functions.

Its other danger is that, even in pure form, it is highly addictive and regular users need ever-increasing amounts to feed their habit. In time, their lives become so dominated by the need to buy more heroin that they are unable to think of anything else. Obtaining and using the substance becomes a full-time occupation in itself. Since users are not able to hold down jobs for long, obtaining the necessary money is a constant problem. As its use is so closely related to crime, eventually all heroin addicts will become criminals and liars. Users soon turn into thieves, although before their addiction developed they may have been horrified at the thought of stealing anything. But in time nearly all users will have to steal to support their habit. Almost all female heroin-users, and not a few male users, turn to some form of prostitution.

Violent crime is not usually associated with heroin use or supplies, but severe penalties for importation and selling, both here and in America, have not so far proved an effective deterrent. There is enough big money in it for pushers to take the risk.

Although the drug carries such a high addiction potential, more harm results from adulterated supplies, dirty needles, a bad diet, poverty, and the very bad housing conditions which those addicted are prey to, than from the substance itself. In time, many addicts become as hooked on their lifestyle as to the drug itself — they become members of a close-knit, though perhaps outcast, fraternity.

The effects of heroin

In its pure form heroin is a narcotic white crystalline powder derived from morphine. It relieves pain and quickly produces dependency, which usually develops within five to eighteen months of starting the habit. As heroin is very short-acting it must be taken often to avoid withdrawal symptoms; these include shaking, sweating, vomiting, muscle aches and spasms. Without treatment, physical symptoms of addiction will disappear within about two weeks. Ex-users have said that withdrawal is something like very bad flu — nasty, but not the agony it is often thought to be.

Medically, heroin and the other opiates are used to depress the central nervous system. For addicts, heroin blocks out mental and physical pain by producing a feeling of euphoria that is more strongly felt at the time than any pain. It alters the perception of pain, although it does not actually take it away. As the dose gets ever higher, and increased amounts are being taken, the user becomes more sleepy and sedated. A classic sign of a heroin user is in the eyes — tiny, pinpoint pupils; in jargon, this is known as 'pinned'. The body comes to expect, and even demand, the drug in time so that severe withdrawal symptoms are experienced between six to twelve hours of taking the previous dose.

Heroin has a high addiction potential because it affects the opiate receptors found in the brain and body. About ten years ago it was discovered that the brain produced its own painkillers. These substances, known as 'endorphins' or 'endogenous morphines', are found in abundance in those areas of the brain which deal with pain and emotion. Every psychoactive drug affects brain cells, to their detriment, and heroin is no exception.

Heroin's main effect on the brain is that it causes production of the natural painkiller to cease. This happens because the body perceives that there is now an ample supply of painkillers coming from outside. The exogenous (coming from outside) drug satisfies the body's opiate receptors. This means that, when the effect of the heroin wears off, there is neither a supply of the endogenous nor the exogenous drug available. Then severe withdrawal symptoms start, as the brain and body are both deprived of a substance that is essential for a feeling of well-being. It has been estimated that the body cannot return to normal physiological functioning for six months after heroin has been stopped. This is even longer in the case of methadone, the substitute heroin-like drug that is often used in the treatment of addicts.

Continued use of heroin also disrupts a wide range of bodily functions. It causes constipation, sickness, liver complaints and wasting of muscles. Hepatitis, a serious liver condition, is a very real risk when heroin is injected, and in fact many users succumb to this disease. Poisoned arms also often result from injecting with dirty needles; few addicts take the trouble to sterilize needles. In women, periods usually stop and in men impotence is a common side-effect. But although menstruation stops in women, ovulation still occurs and pregnancy is possible. Another danger of heroin abuse for women is that, while on the drug, they become dull, lethargic and uncaring, and may not think to take contraceptive precautions. Pregnancy is a common unwanted side-effect of heroin addiction which leads to women then giving birth to heroin-addicted babies.

There has been some suggestion that heroin users may have genetic defects in their endorphin systems, and this puts them at extra risk of dependency. Drugs are now being developed which are supposed to prevent the worst symptoms of opiate withdrawal by encouraging the production of endogenous opiates once more.

Opiates and their synthetic derivatives are often referred to collectively as 'opioids'. They can all be swallowed, dissolved in water and injected or, in the case of heroin, sniffed up the nose like cocaine. This method is known as 'chasing the dragon' and is rapidly becoming the most popular way of taking the drug.

Injection, though by far the quickest way of obtaining the

desired effect, is less widespread than used to be the case. It is also the most dangerous method, partly because clean, sterile needles are rarely used, and partly because injecting leads to almost instant dependence. It produces an effect within seconds and before long the actual ritual of injecting becomes as important to the user as the actual drug. Junkies have been known to inject themselves with anything — vinegar, cold cream, talcum powder — whatever is to hand.

All opioids in Britain are controlled under the Misuse of Drugs Act 1968, which means that it is illegal to supply or possess them without a prescription, or to produce or export them without a specific licence. Heroin, morphine, opium, methadone, dipapone and pethedine all come under Class A of this Act, and codeine and dihydrocodeine under Class B. Another opiate, dextropropoxyphene, is classified as a C drug.

Like other sedatives, opiates depress all nervous system functions, including coughing, heart-rate and breathing. They also dilate blood vessels, giving a feeling of warmth and comfort. They depress bowel function, and cause all bodily systems to become lethargic and slow. Overdosing produces a coma, and is more likely to be dangerous if other drugs are used at the same time, as they very often are. All opiates induce a feeling of drowsiness, and their effect was well described as long ago as 1700 by a London physician, John Jones. In a book called *The Mysteries of Opium Revealed,* he said:

> It causes a most agreeable, pleasant and charming sensation about the region of the stomach, which if one lies or sits still, diffuses itself in a kind of indefinite manner. It has been compar'd, (not without good cause) to a permanent gentle Degree of that Pleasure, which Modesty forbids the naming of.

Present-day addicts of heroin say that the substance makes all pleasurable sensations extremely intense. In the early days of addiction there is often a feeling of intense euphoria which is, apparently, far more pleasurable than the greatest orgasm. But that is only at first. Addicts who have been on heroin for several years do not continue to find pleasure in the substance. All that remains for them is the prevention of withdrawal symptoms, and a certain allaying of anxiety.

Those who are not addicted to heroin, but are given it for analgesic purposes, often intensely dislike its action, as they say it has a dissociating and deadening effect. In 1968 two British doctors decided to take heroin to see what effect it had on them. One of them, Ian Oswald, kept a diary, and published parts of it in the *British Medical Journal*. He wrote:

We've been on heroin a week now, Stuart and I. Seven days of voluntary illness. And how ill we feel. All to settle a theoretical point. . . . My personal view at present is just one made grey and utterly grim by heroin. The extraordinary thing is that it brings no joy, no pleasure. Weariness, above all. At most, some hours of disinterest — the world passing by while you just feel untouched. Even after the injection there is no sort of a thrill, no mind-expansion nonsense, no orgiastic heights, no Kubla Khan. A feeling of oppressed breathing, a slight flush, a sense of strange unease, almost fear of the unknown. . . . Unsteady and uneasy you walk to the door and down the stairs. Stand and stand, trying to micturate; eventually in a series of brief spasms succeeding. Into bed and the cold sheets set off an uncontrollable shivering and chattering of teeth, fingers blanched white . . . Why should people take this stuff? Not for joy. Only for an hour of sudden shafts of panic and itching. . . . Now it's 16 hours since the last injection. Withdrawal symptoms are not bad, merely noticeable. The ever-present feeling of weariness just that much worse. A headache, yawning, shiverings and cold feelings, a nose that feels like a common cold, yawning again, hands a little shaky, and poor in grip . . . Never do this again.

After he stopped taking heroin Dr Oswald recorded:

It's a month now since we stopped the stuff, though some measurements (of the effect) continue. It's been wonderful to feel fit and relish life again.

This description shows that heroin does not necessarily confer any pleasurable sensations at all. But, of course, the doctors were taking the stuff for purely scientific purposes, and were watching their reactions closely all the time. As heroin is essentially a depressant, it tends to be sought out by those who already feel some great inner anguish. The substance blocks out pain more effectively than most chemicals, which is why it is still used for terminal cancer patients.

Methadone, the substitute heroin-like drug often used to treat addicts, has an action very similar to the real stuff, and is quite as addictive. Methadone is usually taken orally, though it can be injected, and is available only on prescription. Only a very few doctors are allowed to prescribe heroin these days, but any GP can give the substitute. Whether this imitation drug really can wean addicts off their drug dependence is open to question, but methadone possesses two qualities that actual heroin does not have: it can prevent heroin withdrawal symptoms without conveying any euphoric effect, so is less pleasant to take, and it is long-lasting.

One dose of methadone is equal to five or six heroin shots and, of course, there is not the accompanying ritual of preparing the fix, with all its sensations of restlessness, impatience and panic, followed by euphoria and sedation. Originally formulated in America during the 1960s methadone simply replaces one addiction with another, and parents should not imagine that their child is on the way to being cured if he or she is going to the doctor for methadone.

As a black market has grown up in heroin, so it has with methadone and many addicts sell their supplies to other addicts. In certain parts of America now methadone addicts actually outnumber heroin addicts, so it cannot be considered an effective form of treatment. In this country some users have the idea that methadone is better, or at least less dangerous, than heroin. They like to believe it is a step towards a cure, as its effects are less pleasurable than heroin. There is a feeling that they are giving something up.

After heroin
Many people grow out of both heroin and methadone dependence by the age of about thirty, without any treatment. But it should not be assumed that this means they are no longer addicts. Both drugs, it appears, can easily lead on to alcoholism and many middle-aged alcoholics have been drug-dependent in their youth. Drink, however, is more socially acceptable and as they get older many former drug addicts feel the need to become more 'respectable'.

An established habit of either heroin- or methadone-taking plays havoc with a wide range of mental and physical functions. But there is another big danger, one which cannot be plotted on a graph or described in symptomatic terms: namely, that when people start taking powerful drugs to alleviate any real or imagined pain, this can make them intolerant of any bodily or emotional discomfort at all. One reason why it is particularly hard to wean addicts off their fix is that, as soon as the slightest crisis looms, they will be tempted to return to their former panacea.

Users can find it hard to tolerate anything like bad news in the post, a crick in the neck, stiff joints, a late train, red traffic lights, or any minor inconvenience in life. The merest setback to plans or hopes can send them in search of the drug again. This is the most seductive and the most dangerous effect of heroin dependence.

A purely physical addiction to heroin can be overcome in a matter of months and the body enabled to return to its normal functioning. Human systems have remarkable powers of self-recovery. But breaking the psychological addiction — the need to return to an artificial comforter in times of stress — is a difficult task indeed. And this is where the real insidiousness lies. Although heroin can harm many body organs, by far the worst damage the drug does is to the personality of the user. It takes away an individual's innate coping powers, and leaves people without the inner resources to handle everyday life.

Jargon words

As with other enclosed groups, heroin addicts have their own jargon to describe drug taking. Here is a guide to the main terms used.

Heroin is known as: Skag, smack, gear, Big H, Uncle Henry, Junk, Happy Dust, Happy Powder, Angel Dust.

Injecting the Drug is known as: fixing, shooting up, mainlining, cranking up, jacking up, hitting up. These are all terms used for injecting with a hypodermic needle.

Chasing the Dragon: this means inhaling heroin fumes after melting the powder on silver foil.

Scoring: buying drugs.

Works: syringe, needles, and any equipment needed for using the drug.

Snorting: this refers to cutting the powder into a thin line and sniffing through the nose via a tube or straw.

Snowball: 'cocktail' of heroin and cocaine.

Working: stealing to get money to buy drugs.

Roasting, Cold Turkey: withdrawal from heroin, with accompanying symptoms which may include dizziness, stomach cramps, muscle pains, nausea, sweating and headaches.

The Cure: going to bed for two or three days while symptoms last, with plenty of hot drinks, and someone to 'talk you through it'.

Cutting: adulterating heroin with other substances which look similar.

Coming Clean: taking the cure to come off heroin.

The Man: term for heroin dealer.

Pusher: a type of dealer who tries to get new people hooked on drugs to increase business.

Habit: heroin addiction.

Script: a doctor's prescription, either for heroin itself or the substitute.

Flipping Out: going berserk, turning into an animal while on heroin.

Ratsacked, Busted: being raided by the police.

Skagsville, Loopy Land, Junk City: the heroin world.

Skaghead, Junkie: addict.

Being Stoned: the effect while on drugs.

Cannabis

Cannabis comes from a hemp plant which grows all over the world. Its tops produce marijuana and the resin forms the basis of hashish. It is often used to produce a drug effect in those countries where alcohol is forbidden, and very few places in the world allow the legal use of both substances.

The non-therapeutic use of cannabis began in earnest among students during the 1960s, and those who continued with the drug appeared to be people who had limited emotional resources to cope with emotional stress. These days, only a very few young people will not have experimented with cannabis but, at the same time, hardly any will use it on a regular basis.

Although it is not physically addictive, meaning that the body comes to rely on it for its day-to-day functioning, cannabis may produce a psychological dependence. There can be distinct reactions, the commonest of these being that many people who use cannabis regularly become extremely lazy and do not want to work, or exert themselves at all. The effect of cannabis is that of a mild intoxicant, and the drug still accounts for nearly eighty per cent of all drug offences in the UK.

Over the past eighty years, according to the leaflet produced by Release, the long-established drug advice charity, there have been thirteen major national and international enquiries into the effects of this plant, including our own government-sponsored report, which came out in 1968. Even so, there is still not complete agreement as to how dangerous cannabis is and whether it has any long-lasting effects.

A report in the *British Medical Journal* in 1980 concluded that cannabis was definitely 'not harmless'. It has been suggested that the substance can cause brain damage, and that it is illogical to consider it a safe and mild drug. But, at the same time, cannabis can be of use in certain cancer treatments, as can many of the psychoactive drugs.

Cannabis smoke contains many substances similar to those found in tobacco, so it cannot be considered a safe alternative to cigarettes. It is the considered view of Dr Norman Doorenbos, of Illinois University, that 'pot' can cause genetic damage by interfering with the chemical balance of DNA. It can also impair fertility, cause lung damage and create psychological problems such as impaired concentration and a feeling of apathy or being 'laid back'.

One of the main problems with cannabis, as with any illegal drug, is that supplies are liable to be adulterated. Its main active ingredient, tetrahydrocannibol, can vary enormously from one batch to the next. Smoking cannabis can be rather like having a glass of beer that may contain either no alcohol or the equivalent of several pints. As there is no form of quality control, you do not necessarily have any real idea of what you are smoking.

It seems reasonably certain that cannabis is toxic, at least to some extent, but its long-term effects are still not understood. One of the reasons for this is that, as the drug continues to be outlawed in most Western countries, there have never been enough people admitting to taking it for large-scale clinical trials to be conducted. Cannabis users themselves rarely seek medical aid to come off the drug, and do not consider themselves addicts in any way. No cannabis user feels he or she has a drug 'problem'.

Effects

The substance can cause an increase in pulse rate, a drop in blood-pressure, a dry throat and a feeling of tiredness. One or two joints smoked properly — that is, taking the smoke deep into the lungs and holding it there for a few seconds — will produce the desired effect. But new smokers will very often experience nothing at all for the first few joints.

It must also be borne in mind that the drug will not affect all users in exactly the same way. Although for many people cannabis is a pleasant, mood-enhancing experience, for some, the substance can cause the most severe reactions. Jane Smith, writing in *The Guardian* in 1984, described how a harmless-looking hashish cake sent her into agonizing spasms, interspersed with bouts of unconsciousness, for about forty-eight hours. Yet her husband, sister, and brother-in-law, who also enjoyed slices of the same cake, were completely unaffected.

'Respectable' adults generally frown on and condemn cannabis even though, many years ago, it acquired a reputation as the non-drug of the century. Although perhaps the least addictive of the mind-altering chemicals it can, according to Professor Griffith Edwards, Professor of Addiction Behaviour at the University of London, cause short-term psychosis, impair driving ability and cause permanent loss of the short-term memory faculty if taken on a regular basis.

The important question for parents is: can cannabis taking lead to a drug habit becoming established which will in time lead to harder drugs being tried? There seems no absolute answer to this. In its leaflet *Drug Misuse*, prepared for professionals and all people who need detailed information on drug use today, the DHSS inclines to the view that people who use cannabis are more likely to try other drugs. Furthermore, the leaflet adds, those who smoke tobacco or drink are more likely to try cannabis. Using one drug does not actually cause people to use another in a direct way, although the habit of taking in drug-like substances can be established. Regular users can come to feel a psychological need for the effects of the drug, or rely on it to ease social occasions, rather like alcohol.

The Release leaflet on cannabis indicates that taking the drug does not lead to harder drugs being tried. It is easily the most commonly taken of the illegal drugs, and there are probably at least a million occasional cannabis users in this country. The law states that it is illegal to cultivate, produce, supply or possess this drug, unless a Home Office licence has been granted for research purposes. It is also an offence for premises to be used for producing, cultivating, supplying or smoking cannabis. It should be said that these laws have made little difference to the prevalence of the substance.

For many years now, there has been a campaign to legalize cannabis. Release are in favour of this and say in their leaflet that, 'there appears to be no justification for spending money on apprehending, processing and maintaining in institutions people whose behaviour cannot be shown to be detrimental to others or themselves.' The fact remains however that, whatever people's private opinion of cannabis, the drug is illegal and there are no signs that this situation will be altered in the near future.

The price of imported cannabis at present is between £30 and £35 an ounce for the herbal variety, and between £14 and £25 a quarter-ounce for the more potent resin. About half a gram of resin — one-sixtieth of an ounce — would be enough to make two cigarettes. This could make two or three people mildly intoxicated.

An experienced user can maintain a cannabis 'high' for between two to three hours but with new users very often no effects are experienced at all. It seems that you have to learn about the effects of this drug and using it to maximum advantage takes time and practice. People smoke cannabis to make them more talkative, witty, relaxed and to heighten perception of sound and colour.

There is little danger of a fatal overdose and the worst effect an inexperienced user can have is a feeling of panic. Those who use the drug when they are feeling anxious or depressed may experience unpleasant rather than pleasant sensations.

Cannabis has been used since the dawn of time, particularly in Eastern countries, to heighten perception, and also in religious ceremonies. Its social use has become widespread in Europe and North America over the past thirty years and continues to grow. The main forms of cannabis are: *marijuana,* also known as grass, weed, pot or ganga, which consists of the dried leaves and tops of the plant; *cannabis resin,* also known as hash, or charas, which is the sticky resin from the upper leaves collected and pressed into blocks; and *cannabis oil,* produced by refining the resin.

The resin is the most commonly used form in Britain, and marijuana is more widespread in America. In its various forms it can be smoked or eaten, or the leaves brewed into a kind of tea. It can be smoked either on its own, or mixed with tobacco and rolled up into cigarette papers. The cigarettes are known as 'joints' or 'reefers' and the butt of a cannabis cigarette is called a 'roach'.

Cocaine

Cocaine is used mainly by rich and upper-middle-class people, and has acquired the reputation of being the drug that film stars and beautiful people prefer. As it is expensive it is not generally a young person's drug, but it is very much part of the smart set in America. Recently, however, there have been reports of large amounts of cocaine entering the UK, and it appears that its use in this country is very much on the increase.

The action of cocaine is directly opposite to that of most other illegal drugs in that it stimulates the central nervous system. It is extracted from the leaves of the coca plant, which grows mainly in South America. Cocaine creates a psychological rather than a physical dependence.

It is usually sold as a white crystalline powder and snorted — sniffed — up into the nostrils or injected. Its immediate action is to constrict the blood vessels and increase heart-rate and blood-pressure. There is an immediate rise in body temperature and a feeling of euphoria and confidence is soon generated. There is arousal of all body systems, and most users experience a sensation of great physical and mental strength. When sniffed the effects are at their height after fifteen to thirty minutes, then they start to wear off. To maintain the effect, a dose may have to be repeated every twenty minutes or so.

Between 1970 and 1980, the use of cocaine was popular mainly in artistic and musical circles, but now the age range is coming down and its rapidly decreasing price is making it come second to heroin in youth appeal. This is in fact where the largest increase is occurring. Pure cocaine costs between £50 and £70 a gram, and a new user might take a quarter of a gram over a weekend. Tolerance increases, and a fully fledged user may consume one or two grams a day.

Effects

Cocaine has long been popular with ambitious people as, above all, it is the drug that delivers a feeling of power and being in control. Users will say that the stuff makes them feel good in very specific ways. Rather than simply blotting out pain and depression, as heroin tends to do, cocaine makes people feel optimistic, intelligent and successful. Using it implies that you are special, as it has acquired a glamorous reputation.

A cocaine 'high' lasts from ten minutes to an hour, depending on the dosage, and afterwards, depression, irritability and extreme pessimism may set in. Overdosing is common, and cocaine deaths — usually by heart failure — are not at all rare. The substance puts a continual strain on the heart and can cause irregular heartbeats, strokes and embolism. Cocaine can also cause brain seizures.

It has been called the 'sex drug' and its chemical effect can closely resemble sexual arousal. Snorting, the most common way of taking cocaine, is an elaborate ritual whereby powdered cocaine is poured into two thin lines on a mirror or other silvered surface. A straw is then inserted into each nostril, and the high may occur within seconds. Repeated use can irritate sensitive membranes in the nose and throat, and cause decreased resistance to colds and flu. After a time, nosebleeds are common and permanently blocked-up sinuses can result.

The other popular way of taking cocaine is known as freebasing. In this method, the drug is cooked to make it more potent, then dried. This 'freebase' is then smoked in a glass pipe and it produces an instantaneous effect, which users say is better than the best orgasm ever. It also produces irritation of the tongue and can cause permanent damage to the mouth, throat and lungs.

Injecting cocaine is not common, but it is the most direct way of obtaining a high. This method is also the most dangerous as it can deliver a punch which actually stops the heart from beating. Apparently, the feeling is like coming off a roller coaster at high speed: you get a roaring and ringing in the ears, and a kind of manic joy results.

As with other illegal drugs, there is no guarantee of the purity of cocaine which is bought in the street. It can contain bacteria, or be cut with other chemicals. When this happens, dangers of severe health damage are intensified. Cocaine users are usually very thin, pale, permanently hyped-up and are very often unable to form stable relationships. As with heroin, relationships in any cocaine-taking set tend to form round the substance itself. Addicts may not have much in common with each other, and there is very often no real friendliness or closeness. Users are united only in their use of the drug.

The substance tends to be taken by people who want to feel good all the time and who have not realized that life does not admit of this feeling on a permanent basis. Cocaine takers are those who become impatient when life does not conform to their — often unreal — expectations. It is possibly a drug taken more by extroverts than introverts, as it intensifies outward-going behaviour.

Medically, cocaine has very restricted uses indeed and, as with heroin, a doctor must be licensed by the Home Office to prescribe it. It is not so physically addictive as heroin, but users can come to rely on the feelings of physical and mental well-being imparted by the drug. But as use continues, the unpleasant feelings may become more frequent than the desired effects. Instead of euphoria, restlessness, nausea, over-excitability and insomnia may set in. If users persist, there may be further worsening of symptoms to include a type of paranoid psychosis. A continuous feeling of exhaustion is common.

After people stop taking cocaine, however, all these adverse effects clear up, and there may well be no long-term damage.

Amphetamines

These are synthetic powders which came into widespread use during the 1950s and '60s as a prescription drug for depression. They were also, at one time, widely used as slimming pills. Medically, amphetamines are now used only for sleepiness and, paradoxically, for hyperactive children. They are a stimulant, and their action is similar to that of cocaine. They may be swallowed in tablet form, dissolved in water and injected, or even smoked, but the most common method nowadays is to sniff them up the nose. They are prescription-only drugs, and their use is very strictly controlled.

Amphetamine tablets have been used for military purposes, and in the Vietnam war it is estimated that US soldiers used 225 million amphetamine tablets to keep them fighting fit. Tolerance to amphetamine or 'speed' soon develops, and most of the stuff available on the black market will have been illegally manufactured, in the form of amphetamine sulphate. This comes either as a white crystalline powder, or in blue and white pills.

Amphetamines increase heart-rate and raise blood-pressure and blood sugar levels. Most people who take them report that they feel more cheerful and energetic and have increased confidence and alertness. They can also feel more ready to face the world. Euphoria is followed, fairly quickly, by a strong let-down in the form of depression and tiredness. Amphetamines can improve performance in boring or repetitive tasks for a short time and, when under the influence, thinking may appear to be profound.

This is a delusion, however, as most people talk gibberish when taking these pills. Amphetamines were placed on the poisons list in 1939 and are now controlled under the Misuse of Drugs Act. When used, the body's energy stores become quickly depleted. During an amphetamine trip anxiety and panic attacks can follow euphoria. Tolerance is soon built up and gradually increased doses are necessary to maintain the desired high. Habitual use carries the risk of damaged blood vessels, and a psychotic state is a very real risk.

Large quantities of amphetamines are easily available on the black market, and the cost is £10 to £15 a gram. A first-time user may take half a gram, but a seasoned addict can get through one or two grams a day. Effects last for three to four hours, after which the user comes down, usually with feelings of profound tiredness. It can take two days to recover fully.

LSD

LSD — the letters stand for lysergic acid diethylamide — is made from ergot, a fungus growing on rye, and was discovered in 1938. In the 1960s, it became almost sanctified as the drug that could open up hitherto closed areas of the unconscious, and bring long-buried fears to the surface. Like alcohol, it can reduce critical faculties. There is less interest in LSD now than in the 1960s, although its use continues to some extent.

There is little evidence that moderate use of LSD can lead to any serious organic damage. The drug is controlled under the Misuse of Drugs Act, and comes in Class A. This means it is illegal to produce, supply or possess the substance, which has no therapeutic uses. LSD-containing tablets are not expensive and cost between £1.50 and £2.50 each (in 1985). A trip begins from half an hour to an hour after taking the stuff, and rises to its peak after two to six hours. Then the user begins to come down.

The effects perceived depend very much on the mood of the user at the time, but they often include seeing intensified colours and visual or auditory distortions. Actual hallucinations are rare. There may be a feeling of heightened self-awareness and a perception of some mystical and ecstatic experience. A common feeling is of being outside the body.

A bad trip may include depression, dizziness or panic. Deaths from overdosing are unknown. The drug is not physically addictive and the main dependence is psychological. While under the influence, co-ordination can be poor and concentration is limited. Usually, the first trip is the best, and thereafter experiences decline. This means that its use is self-limiting. Most people give up LSD a very short time after experimentation, and prolonged use is very rare.

Barbiturates

Barbiturates, which have faded from the public gaze somewhat, are still taken non-medically in some circles, mainly by very young people. They are a hypnotic drug, and can be very dangerous. Between 1959 and 1974 over 27,000 people in this country died from barbiturate poisoning, during which time there were 225 million prescriptions issued for this drug under the brand names Tuinal, Seconal and Nembutal. Since January 1985 barbiturates have been controlled under the Misuse of Drugs Act, and come in Class B. Doctors may still prescribe them but otherwise their use and possession is now illegal.

There does not appear to be a huge black market in barbs and most supplies come from prescriptions, from recognized pharmacies. The drugs can be injected, and one study in 1978 showed that barbiturates were a cause of death in fifty-three per cent of drug-related deaths in London. But as drug companies have increasingly replaced them with benzodiazepines (tranquillizers) their use has declined sharply.

Barbiturates depress the central nervous system and act as a sedative, in much the same way as alcohol. The effect can last for between three and six hours. A small dose has a relaxing effect, but with larger doses the user soon feels extremely sleepy. Control of speech and body movement can be lost, and there may also be severe mood swings and confusion. With larger doses unconsciousness is a very real risk, and fatal overdoses have not been uncommon in the past. Ten pills can be enough to cause death, and, in any case, hazards are greater when alcohol is taken as well.

As with any sedative drug, increased doses become necessary to maintain the effect. Withdrawal may be difficult and can include such side-effects as irritability, twitching, sleeplessness and convulsions. Permanent brain damage may result from prolonged use. Long-term users may be more prone to bronchitis and pneumonia, also overdosing. Injecting sedatives is possibly the most hazardous form of all drug abuse.

Solvents

Solvent sniffing is the term used when chemicals contained in aerosol sprays, paint thinners, superglues and petroleum by-products are inhaled to produce an alteration of mood. When sniffed, the effects are experienced literally within seconds. Many users report that there is an instant mood enhancement and feeling of well-being. The 'high' produced by the sniffing of volatile substances contained in aerosol sprays and glues lasts from five to fifteen minutes and is very similar to alcohol, with the important difference that there is usually no hangover afterwards.

One of the biggest dangers with solvent or glue-sniffing is that these chemicals are easily available. There tends to be little suspicion when a teenager goes into a shop apparently to buy ordinary household items. None of the substances contained in the products used for sniffing are illegal or expensive and, possibly for this reason, the subject has aroused far less hysteria and controversy than heroin. But in fact the chemicals contained in these ordinary household products can adversely affect many body systems.

Sniffing aerosol sprays can cause laryngeal spasms and freeze vocal cords. The inhalants can act as powerful depressants of the central nervous system and produce an intoxication that is virtually identical to alcohol. These effects are: increased excitement, loss of inhibition, a sense of euphoria, dizziness, impaired judgement and even hallucinations. The toxic effect is usually short lived, but continued inhalation of fluorocarbons — a dangerous group of chemicals contained in some solvents — can, on rare occasions, lead to heart failure.

There is, however, no long-term physical or psychological dependence. Experimentation is most common among the twelve to sixteen age group and by far the vast majority of solvent sniffers are boys, who outnumber girls by ten to one. Sniffing is almost exclusively confined to those from poor or working-class backgrounds, both here and in America. Sniffers very often, although not always, come from backgrounds where there is a history of child abuse or neglect, and from low-income, one-parent families. As solvents mimic the action of alcohol so closely, there is a greater risk of children experimenting with these substances where one or both parents are heavy drinkers.

The British government has now launched schemes and produced explanatory leaflets which will, it hopes, help to stem the tide of this growing problem. In Scotland it is now an offence to sell solvents to children if misuse is suspected, but apart from this there is no restriction on sales.

There are three main types of synthetically-developed chemicals that can cause a high when sniffed. They are: volatile solvents, such as those used in certain strong glues; benzene, used in petrol and allied substances such as lighter fuel; and propellants, composed of fluorocarbons, which are used in aerosol cans. Among the substances that can cause alteration of consciousness when sniffed are: varnish remover, hairspray, paint thinners, glues, cement for plastic model making, and thinner used in error corrector fluid for typewriters.

Solvents are sniffed by being placed in a plastic bag with its open end against the nose and mouth and taking in the fumes. In essence, solvent sniffing, which has quickly earned itself a downbeat reputation, is no different from laughing gas, ether and chloroform, which were all inhaled for similar reasons a hundred years ago.

For most teenagers, according to the Release leaflet on the subject, solvent sniffing is an adolescent phase which soon passes and which does not lead automatically to more serious drug dependence in later life. The DHSS leaflet on drug misuse says that psychological dependence may develop in a small minority of susceptible youngsters, especially if they have family or personality problems. Deaths caused by solvent sniffing are rare; although in 1984 the death was reported in Trowbridge, Wiltshire, of a fourteen-year-old girl who had become addicted to glue. Commenting on this case, a Trowbridge social worker said: 'Youngsters are turning to glue because they are bored and have little prospect of work.'

Most doctors and drug experts are of the opinion that solvent sniffing is unlikely to cause permanent damage to vital organs, as it is usually carried on for such a short time and at a period when there can be quick recovery. There was a case reported in 1966 of a man who had been sniffing a whole gallon of solvent toluene every few weeks for about fourteen years, after which, not surprisingly, he died. This story has passed into solvent-sniffing folklore, and is issued as a dire warning to those who may be tempted to try the stuff.

The fact that solvent sniffing is not physically addictive, and may not lead to serious hard drug addiction later, does not mean that the substances are harmless. Long-term exposure to benzene, found in petrol and rubber solutions, may lead to liver damage, and continuous exposure to tetracholorathane, found in cleaning fluids, has been associated with damage to liver, kidneys and intestines. If aerosols are sprayed directly into the mouth or nose the whole substance, rather than just the fumes from the solvent, is then inhaled. This could possibly cause suffocation, or damage to the lining of the lungs.

According to Release, there is little danger of a teenager becoming physically hooked on solvent sniffing. Once people have given it up, there is usually little incentive to return to the habit. But it is possible that once people have experienced the artificial high that can result from solvent sniffing a mental need to continue with some form of intoxication could be established. However, the real dangers from sniffing appear to be connected with the accidents that may happen while under the influence, rather than from the chemicals themselves. While intoxicated, young people can fall off balconies, into rivers, or march straight out in front of a car. The effect may be heightened if solvents are mixed with alcohol, but otherwise the effects disappear within half an hour of stopping sniffing.

3.

ADDICTS AND THEIR FAMILIES

Who Becomes an Addict?
When we speak of drug addiction we tend to conjure up images of jobless, rootless young people. Yet until the 1960s most registered drug addicts were actually middle-aged or elderly people who had been prescribed morphine for severe pain. There were less than 500 of these. In 1950, there were only twenty-five registered non-therapeutic heroin addicts in Britain. The first sign of increase came in 1951 and by 1959 there were forty-seven notified addicts. Numbers really started to grow rapidly in the 1970s. In 1971, 774 new drug addicts were registered and by 1983, 2,800 were notified by doctors to the Home Office. During 1983, over 10,000 were notified, and the vast majority of these were on heroin. It is now estimated that there are about 100,000 heroin addicts in Britain, and the numbers may be far higher.

Kenneth Leech, the author of *What Everybody Should Know About Drugs* and a clergyman who has spent several years working with addicts in Soho, feels that although the chemicals that bring about altered states of consciousness may change, people do not become addicts simply because the stuff is available, or there are criminals around to push it. The triads, syndicates and Mafia could not exist to meet the demand unless there was a need for the stuff they sold. No, he says, people become addicts after they have made a conscious choice both to use and to continue with the drug. Heroin is the most worrying drug of the moment, but the real danger, says Revd Leech, lies in the lifestyle that users must pursue in order to keep obtaining their fix.

It should be realized that all people who become drug addicts are trying to deal with deep-seated personal problems. Taking heroin may not be a very advisable or sensible way to block out emotional pain but, for the addict, the temporary sensation obtained does seem to cause the pain to go away. Of course, it's all still there inside, and all heroin does is to cover it up for the time being, but troubles can stay away while the habit continues. In fact, for those hooked, there no longer is any emotional trauma left in their lives, as their whole being has become dedicated to obtaining the next fix. Within a very short time of becoming regular users, the ritual of getting, using and being affected by the drug becomes a full time occupation in itself, leaving no room for troublesome relationships, career decisions, or socially acceptable behaviour.

Many parents worry that their bright, alert and healthy children will turn into hopeless junkies. It is not a problem that the previous generation of parents had to face, on the whole, as heroin abuse — by far the commonest kind now — was virtually unknown in this country until about fifteen years ago. Lack of knowledge and direct experience of the drug means that large numbers of people who are now middle-aged actually know nothing about the realities of the stuff and who in fact is liable to become hooked.

It seems that no class of society, and no teenager, however carefully brought up, is potentially immune. Victims are claimed from the highest to the lowest social classes. Many concerned parents will remember with horror the gaunt face of twenty-nine-year-old heroin addict Charles Tennant — son of one of Princess Margaret's oldest friends — staring out of the papers. Jamie Blandford, son of the Duke of Marlborough, has been an addict, as is the son of actor Gordon Jackson. There are many middle-class professional parents who are now finding that their well-brought up, well-educated and protected children, given every opportunity and privilege in life, have become secret junkies. So does this mean that anybody at all can become hopelessly addicted to heroin — or are there distinct personality types and circumstances which increase the risk?

Childhood Background
A detailed paper on the subject, published in the *New England Journal of Medicine* in 1982, gives some clues. There seems to be some evidence that changing patterns of child rearing and family stability are at least in part to blame for the drug epidemic that faces us now.

It all began in America during the 1960s, when there was an unprecedented upheaval in student life and attitudes. These early drug takers and drug experimenters may have unconsciously passed on attitudes and a way of life that is now affecting their own children. Also, the 1960s were the years of major developments in the pharmaceutical industry and ushered in the era of 'a pill for every ill'. It should be remembered that by far the greatest majority of mind-altering drugs — especially those that are most seriously addictive — have actually been manufactured in laboratories, and are not naturally-occurring substances. This goes for heroin, barbiturates, amphetamines and tranquillizers — the worst abused drugs of today. The drugs made from natural substances — LSD, cannabis and cocaine — are less serious in their long-term effects, and are less likely to promote dependence.

It does appear that there are major differences in attitude between drug users and non-users, and that these may be noticed by perceptive parents long before actual drugs may be tried. Children may turn into addicts if their childhood is characterized by unusual rebelliousness and aggression. Various studies on hyperactive children have indicated that these can easily turn into delinquent, drug-taking teenagers, if the hyperactivity is not brought under control in time. Any parent who has a difficult or unruly child would be wise to take action, in case a drug habit develops. This means doing everything possible to increase the child's sense of self-worth and self-confidence. Those who turn into drug addicts are, above all, people with very little sense of self and who have no confidence in their abilities to succeed. Television may even be a contributing factor. It is estimated that the average American child spends seven hours in front of the television each day, and that British and American parents spend less time with their children than any other nation.

It was the visionary Marshall McLuhan, author of *The Medium is the Massage*, a cult book which had a great vogue in the 1960s, who said that people who spend a lot of time watching television eventually emerge with no awareness of who they are. They become disorientated and can then try to 'find' themselves with the aid of drugs.

According to the NEJM paper potential users, whatever their class of society, are characterized by being more anti-social and deviant than other children of the same age. They also possess fewer religious convictions and have a tendency to become easily depressed. They may actually be identified as 'maladjusted' or grow up with learning difficulties. There is also a greatly increased risk for children whose parents themselves smoke, drink or use mind-altering drugs. In such homes, children will have grown up with the idea that it is normal to take something external to relieve pain, depression, or stress, or simply to cope with everyday life.

There is also likely to be a history of bad relations with parents and a lack of closeness or genuine affection. Actual or emotional absence can increase the risk. Many life histories of heroin addicts will, if you look closely, contain periods when one or both parents were away for significant lengths of time. However, this lack of closeness does not always mean physical absence. Parents who are very hardworking, or high achievers, or are more interested in their own career than the lives of their children, may also discover they eventually have an addict on their hands.

All children want to feel they matter and they may not appreciate it when adults are often away, pursuing careers or a jet-set life. The absence of one parent through death or divorce can also be a risk factor.

Teenagers and Drugs
A well-adjusted, happy, well-motivated teenager may experiment with cannabis, but is unlikely to go on to trying hard drugs. Nor does it seem likely that this same teenager will inadvertently get into the 'wrong' set of people, or deliberately choose as friends those already on heroin. It is far more probable, from all the evidence available, that those who are predisposed towards drug addiction will of their own accord seek out peers who are users. The time-honoured sociological phrase 'peer group pressure' only has reality, in this instance, for those who have made up their minds to try the stuff.

It seems as though the future addict has a 'premorbid' personality, characterized by intense self-dislike. Once on the drug, this trait quickly deteriorates into self-loathing, which may take the form of violent outbursts against those who are nearest and — supposedly — dearest.

It is true that addicts are getting ever younger, and a recent British newspaper report estimated that around eighty per cent of young people living in the depressed area of Wirral, Merseyside, had easy access to heroin and that a substantial number of them were actually using the drug.

The problem is undoubtedly exacerbated by unemployment and a general sense of hopelessness. Here we can draw a parallel with the 1930s, when young people became hooked on fantasy songs and dances. The 1980s addiction is, however, far more serious and difficult to cure.

A recent detailed market research survey commissioned by the DHSS found that the majority of heroin users were male, and that almost all female users had been introduced to the habit by an older male who was already using it. Most at risk were young impressionable girls with an emotionally-deprived home background. They were attracted to the 'outsider' image that heroin possesses. If a girl has a boyfriend who is on heroin, abuse of this drug becomes an integral part of the relationship. It is also possible that those vulnerable to heroin misuse are mutually attracted in the first place. Very often, the first use will be offered free of charge, and the girl is then introduced to a heroin-using circle. The 'evil pusher' image does not appear to be substantiated by fact. The DHSS survey uncovered no evidence at all of users being introduced to heroin in this way.

Most young people will not become users, but for those who are at risk heroin has a glamorous, attractive image. The appeal of heroin is complex. It seems that the desire to try it originally springs from a mixture of curiosity, bravado, and availability. There will also be some perception of the need to alleviate deeply-felt boredom and aimlessness. Users interviewed on the government survey said that heroin was always presented to them as being relatively safe and not as addictive as oldies claimed.

It also seems that most users find their initial experience of heroin extremely enjoyable. However, they are, for the most part, a pre-selected group who are determined to enjoy it. It should always be remembered that perception of what is enjoyable varies greatly from person to person. One individual enjoys ski-ing, another will be terrified of it. Some people love the cinema, some love going to football matches. Others like sitting by the fire and knitting, or eating expensive food in restaurants. So it is with heroin. Perception of its benefits and the enjoyment that comes from taking it varies enormously according to personality, expectations, and the amount of distress that needs to be alleviated. But, although first use may be pleasant, all addicts find that in time the positive benefits disappear. Then it all becomes a desperate bid to forestall the dreaded withdrawal symptoms.

Teenagers who resisted heroin were, in the main, afraid of becoming addicted. Some saw the stuff as being instantly highly addictive, an evil substance that would lead to certain death. Some of the better informed adolescents, who were actually in contact with heroin users, knew that it did not always lead to instant addiction or eventual death, but they feared becoming hooked themselves. This fear kept them off trying heroin even once. For this group of teenagers, heroin addicts were seen as boring, unattractive and morbidly obsessed with themselves. The DHSS survey discovered that the illegality of heroin was not a factor in either use or abstention. Most teenagers did not care one way or the other about whether it was legal.

Those teenagers and young people who feel that they cannot be themselves in ordinary everyday life, and are constrained to play a part, will try to release this true self through heroin. Also, while under its influence, the user is spared from the need to please others, or come up to their expectations. While using you are pleasing only yourself, and escaping to a private world which nobody else can destroy.

Women and Heroin

Although more teenage addicts are male, women often become hooked in later life, in their twenties, unless they have been introduced earlier to the substance by a boyfriend. Women who discover heroin for themselves are often people who wake up to the realization that life has not dealt them a very good hand. No Prince Charming who would magic all problems away ever materialized, and existence has become narrowed to a sordid flat, a couple of kids, no money, and a husband who takes no interest.

DAWN (Drugs, Alcohol, Women, Nationally), a charity devoted to helping women overcome serious addiction problems, has this to say in its leaflet, *Women and Heroin:*

> Women start to use heroin for a lot of different reasons. It cushions us from reality, makes problems fade away and at first can give us confidence and energy. Many women use it in the long term to get through routine tasks, such as housework, coping with a family or a boring job, or to cope with an otherwise intolerable situation.

The leaflet adds:

> Regular use of heroin can become a lifestyle. Scoring, talking about and using heroin can give women a special identity and a sense of belonging to a group, or it can increase our isolation.

All this could apply to young people equally as well. When taking heroin, teenagers can feel they are members of a special secret society, where they can experience feelings denied to them in the 'respectable' outside world. Parents often say wonderingly, when hearing of yet another adolescent who has become hooked on heroin, 'But I can't understand it. They've had every opportunity, every chance.' This may not, however, be how the child saw the situation. The child may perceive herself as lost, alone, and with nobody to talk to. She cannot seem to gain a sense of purpose in life and the heroin, which becomes a total lifestyle in itself, can be a very satisfying solution. As it eventually blots out everything but the need for more and more, heroin takes away the pain of coming to terms with who you are and where you are going.

Heroin can appear to be even more of a whole-life solution for girls than boys, as there are so very many pressures on girls these days. A confused young woman often does not know which way to turn. Should she stay on at school, get good qualifications and aim at a long-term career? Or should she make herself attractive to boys; should she enjoy sex? Should she get married, have children, and become dependent on a man?

All of these questions, which have no easy answers, can be solved at a stroke by taking heroin. Then there can be no question of a career, no question of making yourself attractive, no question of becoming dependent on a man. You are dependent on the heroin instead.

The DAWN leaflet says that heroin users are seen as being deviant and outside society, as heroin is viewed as the very worst drug there is. Actually, heroin is by no means as difficult to withdraw from as people tend to imagine. The worst symptoms disappear within two weeks and will not return. But the great problem for addicts is finding themselves an alternative lifestyle that will be as satisfying and demanding. If a person does manage to come off heroin, what does she do with all that time formerly spent scoring, injecting, snorting or obtaining the stuff — and then being affected by it?

As with every other drug, heroin does not remove underlying personal problems, but replaces them with something else that temporarily makes them insignificant. The problems are still there, lurking underneath, but you do not have to face them. After coming off, addicts have to look again at their original difficulties and inadequacies, which will have actually multiplied during the time they remain on the drug. They will almost certainly be in a bad physical condition, with all their internal organs in a weakened state. If they have been injecting, their livers will be malfunctioning, as will their veins. Many former addicts return again and again to their fix, as they discover that the long road back to health and happiness is too long and arduous for them. It must be said that most drug clinics and agencies have fairly low success rates in the long term.

What Parents Can Do

As always, prevention is better than cure. This is particularly the case with addictions, as these can never be cured — only kept under control.

The best thing that parents of young children can do to prevent a drug problem occurring is to set an example of good behaviour themselves. This means not just abstaining as much as possible from alcohol and tobacco, but instilling a positive attitude into the child. If the emphasis in the home is always 'you can do it' rather than 'you'll never do it', there is a greater chance that the child will grow up with an appropriate sense of self-worth. Those who grow up with an inner, unshakeable core of self-confidence will never turn to drugs, and an easy, open relationship with the parents based on mutual trust and understanding will also help a lot. All young people who become addicts are emotionally deprived, although they may have had every material advantage.

Parents should try to take a detached, relaxed attitude towards their children. It should be remembered that, of all teenagers, only a tiny minority will turn to hard drugs, even though the present numbers are frighteningly huge and are on the increase. You should not assume the worst, that your child will turn to drugs, or get in with a bad set. These 'bad sets', as we have seen, do not happen out of the blue, but are consciously sought by the young person hell-bent on trying out drugs. If there is no interest or temptation in the first place, more stable friends and a different 'set' will be chosen.

The sensible action for a modern parent is to be knowledgeable about the drugs, both legal and illegal, that teenagers are liable to use. Young people repect adults who do actually know what they are talking about and who do not fall into the trap of assuming that all drugs are equally addictive, dangerous and toxic. Most of today's teenagers will try cannabis which, while illegal, cannot be regarded in the same light as heroin and cocaine. Parents often over-react on hearing that their children have smoked a joint of cannabis and issue dire warnings that heroin addiction is only around the corner. But most teenagers who have tried cannabis will never go on to harder drugs, so a condemnatory attitude is bound to be counter-productive.

This does not mean that cannabis-taking is to be condoned. On the contrary, parents should explain that the substance, while probably not physically addictive and harmful to body systems, is nevertheless an alien chemical, and it would be better for the child not to allow it into his or her life. A parent who learns that cannabis-taking is rife at the child's school ought to inform the head teacher and try to work out with the teachers what can be done to minimize the drug habit. In independent schools instant expulsion is the penalty for being caught with cannabis, but this punishment has not acted as a deterrent. It is a good idea for head teachers and others to work out a series of talks on drug abuse and — while avoiding scare stories which have the effect of glamorizing drugs — explain carefully the dangers.

On cannabis parents could say that, although it is not a hard drug, and although many rock stars take it, it is far better to grow up without having to be dependent on an outside chemical for feelings of happiness and well-being. But on the whole a fairly light note should be adopted — reserve harsher words for harsher drugs, if necessary.

The time to find out about drugs is before the child starts taking them. Unfortunately, most parents leave it too late and only acquire the knowledge after their children have become dependent. Wise parents will find out all they can about modern drugs and then sit down with the child to explain exactly what they are. It's rather like sitting down to impart the facts of life — except that it's far less embarrassing. Children should be told that drugs can indeed give a good feeling — after all, if there were no benefits to be gained, why would thousands of people take them? It should be pointed out that at the same time they can lead to a dependence which takes over your life. In time, you can explain, people can come to rely on chemicals to take away all bad feelings, of failure, depression or unrequited love. But point out that it is far better to learn how to marshall one's own resources to cope with life's inevitable disappointments, as this makes people strong and self-reliant, and more attractive to others. Explain that in time drugs can take a person's individuality away and that all addicts eventually become indistinguishable from each other, a race apart.

If you clearly know what you are talking about, the child will respect and listen to you. But you can never order anybody to respect what you are saying — respect has to be earned. The hard-line approach that some fathers take with regard to drugs, 'If I find any drugs in this house, you'll be out on your ear, son' does not work. It's no use resorting to threats, as these will merely underline the teenager's perception that the parent hasn't a clue what he is talking about.

It is true that in the vast majority of cases where drug addiction occurs, the homes are broken, or the stability of the family has broken down. Parents then blame themselves if drugs are taken — but blame does no good at all. It is not automatic that a child from a single-parent home will turn to drugs, and if the relationship has been good, this is still unlikely to happen. The DHSS survey referred to earlier discovered that, while condemning drugs wholeheartedly, most parents were extremely ill-informed about them, and did not know what they were all about. Adults had an idea that heroin was dangerously addictive and health-destroying, but only a tiny minority understood the difference between 'hard' and 'soft' drugs.

Spotting a Drug User

Drug abusers are, on the whole, young people who have a very negative view of themselves and the world. Parents should make sure they do everything they can to instil a sense of direction and purpose. But parents who do discover that their children are taking drugs should never blame themselves for this, as this leads to a depressing spiral that gets nowhere. Recriminations and 'if only' diatribes achieve nothing. In fact, they may serve to turn the teenager even further in the direction of drugs.

Parents can, in advance, find out about the type of help available (a detailed list of agencies, clinics and hostels is given on page 135) and how each type of help works. It is also a good idea to be on constant guard for any early warning signs, as these are so often missed. Suspicion should be aroused if there is a noticeable alteration in attitudes, consciousness or mood. Extreme depression or elation can happen anyway during the teenage years, but if there is manic happiness, followed by black depression, a psychoactive drug may be involved: all drug-induced highs are followed by equal and opposite lows. Unusual sleepiness or drowsiness should also be noted. The classic sign for heroin use is tiny, pinpoint pupils. Other indications that your child may be on drugs include: lost appetite; losing interest in former hobbies, sport, school or friends; telling lies or behaving in furtive ways; money or valuables disappearing; or any unusual smells, stains or marks on the body. Peculiar-looking powders, capsules, heated tinfoil or needles and syringes should also be regarded with extreme suspicion.

Most young users are too clever to leave telltale signs around if they can help it, but they cannot always conceal their mood. Parents who have good reason to suspect that drugs are being used should never ever be cross with their child. This could make the problem bigger. Very importantly, a parent should talk to their spouse or partner about it. Research has shown that where there are two parents present, it is mainly the mother who takes responsibility for the drug habit. Sometimes mothers try everything they can to shield fathers from the knowledge that their child has become drug-dependent. This is a mistake, as you need all the allies you can get.

It is probably a good idea to tell teachers at school, so that they too can be on the look-out for unusual behaviour. Before confronting any teenager with an accusation about drugs, however, try to find out whether anything is seriously bothering them. It could be exams, boyfriend or girlfriend worries, or fears about their own appearance. Parents should show that they are on the child's side and will do all they can to help, without at any time condoning the drug habit.

Any unexplained attacks of nausea or vomiting, headaches or dizziness could also be warning signs. Lots of colds, coughs and chills, streaming eyes, slurred speech and insomnia should also be closely monitored. It is common for parents, on discovering that their child really is taking drugs, to do quite the wrong thing. They may either use anger, and accuse the child of being a hopeless junkie and a no-good person, or take the 'how could you do this to me' line. Both approaches intensify feelings of failure and self-hatred on the part of the user, and will drive the child to seek out more drugs. Parental disapproval serves to add to the already enormous burden that the child is carrying. It's best to decry the habit, without condemning the person. You should show you still love the child, but indicate that you do not love the drug habit.

The Role of the Family

Families Anonymous, the organization run specially for families and relatives of drug users, offers this advice: the best thing you can do is to talk about the situation before teenagers ever get near drugs, and do all you can to build up a feeling of trust. This cannot absolutely guarantee that they will never be tempted, but it does lessen the likelihood. At the same time, all parents should realize that they can never put the necessary determination and motivation into the child, but only ever encourage and be eternally optimistic. As a parent you can never solve the teenager's own problems, you can only be there for help and advice when needed.

There are a few golden don'ts: *don't* lecture, moralize, scold or argue, if you suspect your child is on drugs. Be there to help but never interfere or try to keep your child in at night, or vet his friends. *Don't* lose your temper if you can help it, as this destroys any real chance of being helpful and having your advice listened to. Above all, *don't* try to cover up for the child, or spare her the consequences of using drugs. All parents have a tendency to do this, as they become so ashamed of the drug taker.

One mother told me: 'I became an accomplished liar in a very short space of time, in an effort to shield my daughter from the consequences of her addiction. She had returned home, I told people, to recover from a virus infection. We offered to help her — we were wrong.'

It is hard to watch a much-loved and once happy and healthy child go down the drug route to degradation and despair; but all parents must realize that it is not actually in their power to prevent the user following the habit. If it has not been spotted in the early stages — and the warning signs are easy to miss if the teenager is away from home at college, university or work — the parent may not realize just how great a hold the addiction has.

Most parents in fact say they suspected nothing until their child was hopelessly addicted. Then the road back is long and hard. If your son or daughter seems ill, tired, thin and listless, it is worth considering whether drugs might be involved, especially if the child has already been smoking and drinking for several years. Particularly suspect drug taking if your child is always mysteriously short of money, or wants to sell valuable possessions.

The very hardest thing for parents, but the most vital, is to try to become detached, objective and unemotional. Try to regard the situation as if you were a concerned aunt, or teacher, rather than a parent. Most parents who contact Families Anonymous, usually when a state of utter despair has been reached, do find they have taken quite the wrong approach when they discover their child is on drugs. Although they have the best intentions, their unspoken attitude of 'how could you do this to me' serves only to drive the habit home harder.

One parent who found her way to Families Anonymous says: ' "Where have I gone wrong?" is the first thought which comes into one's mind on learning that one's attractive and intelligent daughter, brought up in a normal happy family environment, has turned to drugs and is now addicted to heroin. As a parent, I have been through absolute hell and despair, and can only hope that my daughter's desire to kick the habit is strong enough for her to take positive action. We failed by not waiting until our daughter had reached the stage of wanting help. I now have to come to terms with the fact that I am completely powerless.'

A father who discovered his daughter was on heroin said: 'My daughter is twenty-eight and has been a heroin addict for eleven years. For the last five years she has tried to kick the habit but failed. We have had it all, the lying and the physical fights. Once when I found a deadly substance and flushed it down the loo, she attacked me physically, shouting that she hated me and would murder me. As a child, she was a cheerful, happy girl full of life, never depressed or down. But, when she started taking drugs, she underwent a personality change and became a stranger to me, a person I no longer knew . . .

'In those days I did not know how to deal with the situation. My reaction was that of an angry and cheated parent. Then that changed into resigned hopelessness and agonizing anxiety.

'Parents and relatives must give all the love and understanding they can. Do not condemn addicts, for they are helpless, sick people and have no power over their disease. And let no one be complacent about this problem, as it can happen to all of us.'

Another mother says: 'I know that I only hindered my son's recovery, due to my lack of knowledge regarding addiction. Like every other parent, I thought I could help him overcome it with love and understanding, not realizing it was an illness that needs professional understanding.'

A mother whose twenty-one-year-old daughter died of a heroin overdose, said: 'I did everything wrong — for a year I covered up and helped my daughter out of debt — then I took a hard line. It seemed to be working as our loving relationship seemed to be returning. My son and I needed help to cope with Ann's problem. The local GP didn't understand, as very few people do. I know I will be riddled with guilt for the rest of my life. Ann had spent 15 months in a clinic — I thought it was the answer to my prayers.'

These sad stories, all from well-educated, middle-class parents, underline the anguish of having a son or daughter who is addicted. Once the habit had taken hold, they realized they were powerless to do anything. All their offers of help were either wrong, or rejected. It's easy to say — don't let the situation get so bad, but less easy to avert it.

Early in 1985, a £2 million campaign was launched in London to advise parents on how to spot early signs that their children are using drugs. One mother, who failed to spot these signs, wrote to *The Standard* as follows:

> There was a rule that no pot should be smoked in our house, although I was not naïve enough to imagine that Sarah hadn't had any. I trusted her — one is apt to trust one's own child. We sometimes had conversations about drugs, and I would always say that the last people on earth I would help would be junkies because their problems were self-inflicted. I thought that addicts should be put into a cell and given an overdose.
>
> The youngsters would smile and say that I was a fuddy duddy. They seemed to think that magic mushrooms, speed, cocaine and LSD were mere experiments that most youngsters tried and aged out of. . . . Sarah became part of a social scene. She slowly became estranged from us. We started getting phone calls demanding money and telling me that Sarah was on heroin — but no names given. I had to learn for my own survival to become detached and unemotional — it wasn't easy. If you are not careful you start living their hell with them — up when they are up and in utter despair when they are down. Sleepless nights waiting for the call 'Your daughter is dead', wondering if at that moment she was fixing — putting a needle into her body.

The painful lesson that this mother had to learn, when her twenty-two-year-old daughter had plumbed the depths of degradation due to heroin addiction, was not to become caught up in Sarah's own misery. That would just drag both of them down further. She added in her article:

> When Sarah returned to England her boyfriend met her and within a few days they were on heroin again. Sarah phoned me and told me. I said, 'Fine, darling, it's your reality. Let me know when you come off it again.'
>
> She came off, and has now been clean for two months. . . . She says that if heroin was put in front of her she can't be at all sure she wouldn't succumb. At least she doesn't bother to lie to me any more,

which is a release for us both. If it is hard for me it is nothing in comparison to her pain.

Parents should also realize that teenagers do not become hooked on drugs in order to punish the parent — they are simply trying to cope with their own misery.

Drugs in the Home

If adults themselves take drugs such as tranquillizers or sleeping pills to help them cope with stress, they should realize that this in itself can encourage a drug habit among the young. One mother who took tranquillizers to help cope with depression noticed that her pills were disappearing. She put two and two together and realized that her eighteen-year-old daughter, who had recently broken with her boyfriend, was taking them. She confronted the daughter, who slammed out of the house, and the tranquillizers were hidden away. Before long, this daughter became involved in the serious drug scene and was on heroin. A family guidance counsellor pointed out to the parents that they had completely over-reacted on the tranquillizer issue. At this stage, it would have been possible to deal with the situation calmly, but instead all that happened was the situation was made far worse. An over-reaction to 'soft' or prescription drugs being taken does not always lead to a drug habit being established, but it is a warning sign. Taking drugs of *any* kind is always a cry for help — wise parents will heed that cry before it is too late.

The biggest panic often sets in when a parent, who may or may not have suspected that drugs were being taken, has to deal with the consequences of an overdose. Most parents are quite ill-equipped to deal with this, as it is outside their own experience. However, there are signs to look out for and certain things that can be done. The first sign that an overdose has been taken is if the youngster is unconscious or in a semi-coma. First of all, make sure he gets fresh air. Turn the youngster on his side and try not to leave him alone, in case he inhales vomit. Ring for a doctor, or dial 999. If you see any suspicious-looking powders, pills or paraphernalia around, keep these to take to hospital. Afterwards, do not be hostile but allow the child the opportunity to talk over the situation, and encourage him to accept help.

To sum up, here are the most important Dos and Don'ts with regard to parental attitudes over drug taking:

- Before condemning any drug habit, make sure you are setting the very best example yourself. It's more likely that teenagers will take drugs if they see adults around them being dependent on alcohol or tobacco.
- Become knowledgeable. Talk with other adults — your spouse or partner, teachers at school — about how you would react if your child was discovered taking drugs.
- Talk to your son or daughter — not just about drugs, but about their hopes for the future, and let them know you are always around if they need a helping hand or shoulder to cry on.
- Don't be unduly suspicious. Keep a watchful eye, without going through drawers, personal belongings or bags. This destroys trust, and may well encourage a drug habit to take hold.

The best attitude to take with regard to drugs is to talk about it without either making drug taking seem a good idea, or a horrific crime. Scare stories serve only to glamorize the subject. You may be convinced that all drugs are dreadful, but your child may have a quite different view. He or she may find them enjoyable and harmless. Unless you genuinely know what you are talking about, don't dwell on the horrors of withdrawal, addiction and overdosing. Your child simply won't believe you — and is then liable to reject everything you say on the subject.

There is no easy path for a parent, and these days nobody can say with complete confidence: 'My child is far too sensible to take drugs.' This is what *all* parents of *all* addicts say at some stage. At every step, it is vital for adults to examine their own attitudes and, if they are in any doubt at all as to how best to behave, contact an organization such as Families Anonymous. They are the experts in advising families and relatives, and their expertise should not be spurned.

In today's society ignorance over drugs is not bliss. The greatest responsibility any parent can take is to find out all they can about drugs, their effects, cost, availability, and the chances of their children taking them. Also, get to know your own child as an independently-functioning individual. However carefully children have been brought up, they cannot be expected to share their parents' attitudes about everything. It is natural for the young to rebel — and drug taking is an easy way of rebelling. It puts people outside respectable society and, for a time, this is what some young people think they want.

4.

DRUG AGENCIES AND CLINICS

If you have been unable to stop your child taking drugs, the next sensible step is to find out what kind of help is available and how it works. GPs in this country have now all been circulated with an explanatory leaflet about heroin addiction, and they should be more knowledgeable now than they were at one time. Since 1969 only a few specially registered doctors have been allowed to prescribe heroin, and the rest can give the methadone substitute.

The original idea behind prescribing either the drug itself or its substitute was that, by making it available through official channels, illegal pushers would be driven out, and supplies could be regulated. At the same time a watchful eye could be kept on all addicts, who would now be under a doctor's constant care. During the 1970s, the number of addicts being treated in this way went up by eight per cent a year.

Although this method of treating addiction was no doubt formulated with the very best intentions, it has not worked at all. Since doctors have been treating by prescribing, the numbers of addicts have gone ever upwards and much of the heroin and methadone now sold comes originally from doctors' surgeries. So doctors have been turned into unwitting pushers of the drug.

While Britain set up hospital drug centres, to treat addicts by prescribing carefully controlled doses of their fix, the rest of the Western world looked on in amazement. In 1974 an American, Horace Freeland Judson, came over to write a book on the subject. In his *Heroin Addiction in Britain* (Harcourt Brace Jovanovich, 1974), Judson says: 'What everybody knows about the British and heroin is that they supply it on prescription to heroin addicts.' Twenty years ago Britain was actually regarded as one of the more enlightened countries in the treatment of heroin addiction. But, by regarding heroin as a medical, rather than a social, problem more addicts than ever before were created.

The situation now is that nobody can agree on exactly how best to treat addiction. The government has earmarked £7 million for a large campaign designed to stem the tide, but drug agencies and those helping addicts scorn this as a laughably small sum. The problem is that most people working in the drug world are battling against too little money and not enough facilities. There are nowhere near enough clinics to go round; one of the reasons for this being that heroin addiction is still widely regarded as self-imposed, unlike certain other illnesses, such as cancer. Many experts working in drug areas believe that addicts should be regarded as sick people who need to be made better, rather than bad people who must be made good.

Most drug agencies are run by charitable concerns, on a shoestring budget, and are always liable to be closed down for lack of funds. This chapter outlines the main drug agencies and clinics, and gives a brief description of how each is trying to meet, at least to some extent, the vast drug problem that faces us now.

Doctors

Often the first line of treatment is through the family doctor. As with other illnesses, some doctors are knowledgeable about heroin addiction, while some know absolutely nothing. But more than this, individual doctors vary very considerably in their attitude towards addicts. Some are sympathetic, while others take the line that addicts deserve all they get. The new DHSS guidelines, issued to doctors in 1984, advise against long-term prescribing of methadone; and the policy of putting addicts on opioid drugs for more than six months has been virtually outlawed. There is now a definite shift away from the old idea that addicts should be maintained on smaller doses.

It has been found that methadone actually perpetuates drug abuse rather than encouraging withdrawal. So nobody who goes to the doctor and is prescribed methadone should in any way look upon it as a cure. The best that this form of treatment can do is to wean addicts away from street supplies, which are liable to be cut, and from using unhygienic needles.

But, as with every story, there are two sides. A GP, Dr Emily Gray, gives her views on trying to help heroin addicts. Writing in *Medical News,* Dr Gray says:

We have had one or two people turning up, claiming to be heroin addicts wanting to get off their horse, so to speak. My partner took immense trouble with them, getting in touch with the Rehabilitation Unit, and learning from the psychiatrist how to prescribe decreasing doses of methadone, for the withdrawal symptoms.

She was treating three of them when the first one whom she had weaned off came back saying that she had gone back on the drug and wanted another course. Her companion wanted another prescription because he had dropped the bottle.

We had read the DHSS spiel saying it was possible for GPs to help addicts and that one should not adopt a nihilistic attitude. But we began to get the impression we were being taken for a ride.

I was therefore prepared when the brother of another addict appeared. His story was that he lived in the middle of the drug using area and he wanted to get off heroin but he could not manage it until he was rehoused out of the way of temptation.

Giving him the address of a Rehabilitation Clinic, I was delighted to be able to tell him he could do it without drugs. [Dr Gray had investigated how Rehabilitation Houses worked, and found they did not believe in prescribing drugs.] Well, he did turn up at the treatment centre and the organiser told him that she did not believe he was using as little as he said. By his weight loss and general pallor, she thought he was on at least a gram a day, or £60 worth a week.

He became very annoyed with her. She did not think he was honest in his stated intentions. . . . It did not sound too hopeful but my health visitor friend has telephoned to say that he has kept his last appointment and has become very, very angry, which is, apparently, a good sign.

Many doctors who genuinely want to be helpful will sympathize with Dr Gray. On the whole, GPs have little experience of treating heroin addicts and not all realize that these people are often devious and deceitful in the extreme. Taking the drug has made them like this, and many will use any opportunity to get further supplies of the drug, either to use or to sell.

But Dr Gray's article in *Medical News* illustrates what, ideally, doctors *should* do. If a heroin addict turns up at the surgery the best course of action for the doctor is to get in touch with the nearest rehabilitation centre, and ask their advice, then send the addict along for treatment. But drug addicts are very, very difficult people to treat. Their addiction has turned them into thieves and liars, and not all doctors or parents will realize this at first.

In the past, many GPs have been extremely nervous of dealing with drug addicts, and not without reason. But now they all have

DHSS guidelines and should, at least, be able to avoid the worst pitfalls.

There are three main types of treatment: giving a substitute drug; 'cold turkey' — instant withdrawal; and spending a few months in a private clinic. Doctors can refer addicts to the nearest hospital clinic, or to an agency such as City Roads.

City Roads

This is an old-established short-term residential drug rehabilitation centre in North London. Addicts may be referred there by doctors, by parents, friends or relatives, or they can come in by themselves. It should be said, however, that there is virtually always a waiting list.

The aim at City Roads is instant withdrawal, and a team of nurses, social workers, health visitors and doctors is on hand to help addicts return to a useful and satisfying drug-free life. City Roads began life in May 1978, since when it has established itself as one of the most successful charitably-run drug agencies in the country.

The director, Giampi Adhaleff, explains how City Roads operates:

> Most calls initially come from friends or relations, rather than the drug user. Then we have to suggest to the friend that the user may not be at the crisis stage. It is part of our job to explain that you can't really ever help somebody unless they are desperate enough to help themselves. At City Roads, we only see the desperate cases.
>
> Parents should not necessarily hit the roof if they discover their child is using drugs. Some people deal with their dependency quite happily and never become true addicts. It should be remembered that drug use is often a passing phase that people grow out of, once the miseries of adolescence have passed. The time to worry is when somebody's entire life is centred round obtaining and using drugs. If they are clearly ruled by their addiction, that is the time to ring us. If the problem has not become bad enough for us to handle, we can still advise people who ring us or we may suggest one of the other agencies.
>
> I would say that anybody who has resorted to injecting themselves needs to be watched, as this method can lead to blocked veins, hepatitis and upset circulation. Infection will be a constant possibility.

The difficulty a friend faces, according to Giampi Adhaleff, is to distinguish between genuine concern and interfering. But if crime and serious addiction are suspected, then immediate help should be sought.

The actual drug that is being taken is not all that important at City Roads. Users who are referred to crisis centres are not, on the whole, using cannabis, but they may be on heroin, cocaine, barbiturates, amphetamines or, more usually, a mixture of anything they can get. Addicts who cannot obtain heroin supplies may turn to using vast quantities of Gee's Linctus, or Dr Collis Browne's Mixture — medicines which sound harmless enough, but which contain opium tincture.

City Roads feels that sensible counselling in schools and colleges can do much to convey the idea that drugs are not an easy way out of life's problems, but are damaging to every aspect of existence: jobs, health and relationships. They do not condone the idea of prescribing heroin or its substitutes to addicts. 'Having received his prescription, the addict will then sell some of his drugs,' Giampi said. 'People can live off their scripts for two or three days.' Some doctors will issue daily scripts in an attempt to prevent this, but it has not significantly lessened the problem.

At City Roads the aim is to get the addict off his fix, instantly. The physical symptoms will disappear after a few days, but breaking the emotional dependence can be very hard. This is why City Roads likes to take people in for three weeks, when they will be able to have experienced counselling. There is the understanding that detoxification is only one step towards keeping people off drugs in the long term, and several of the 250 residents who are there during a year will have been through the programme before. Some people will have been back as many as eight times, but one-third are still drug-free after a year. With heroin and other drug abusers this is considered good, as for many turning to a drug has become the only way they know of coping with any crisis that life may throw up.

Street Agencies

There are about fourteen of these over the country, and their main aim is to seek out drug users who are not already seeking treatment. Most of their clients are young — under twenty-five — and will not be registered or under a doctor's care. Most clients will be pursuing a chaotic lifestyle and many will drift to central London. The *Hungerford Drug Project,* in operation since 1975, is one of the best known of the street agencies. It works to provide information, advice, referral and counselling services to drug users and their families and friends.

There is a staff team of three social workers, and the project also undertakes out-reach work in the West End of London. The Project will provide speakers for schools, colleges, youth groups, doctors or the police, to give information and advice on drug misuse.

Otherwise, advice is offered by telephone or personal contact at the Project's offices near Charing Cross station. Drug users or their families can contact the centre, either for specific advice or for counselling on how to cope with a drug problem. In its annual statement for 1984, the Hungerford Project noted:

> We recognise that for a certain proportion of our clients, giving up drugs is a long-term prospect, and we take account of this by setting more realistic goals for these individuals. Many clients find it hard to trust people, and we create an informal and friendly environment in which they can get to know the agency and its workers before more formal work takes place.
>
> People can ring the project with a specific enquiry, or can make an appointment for a longer interview. Some clients may only need a phone call, or one interview, while others may need help over many months. A large part of the project's work consists of acting as a referral agent: once we have spent time in finding out exactly what help someone needs, we can refer them on to a specialist agency. However, we often continue to maintain contact with that person.

The Hungerford Drug Project, and other street agencies, are friendly, non-frightening places, and many of their staff are themselves young and unstuffy. A young user may find it easier to contact an agency like this, rather than go to the family doctor.

Hospital Clinics

There are about one hundred hospitals all round the country which offer treatment for drug users, and here referral from a GP is essential. Hospitals specializing in this kind of treatment vary greatly. Some have full-time clinics staffed by a well-motivated team of doctors, social workers, psychologists and nurses; whereas other hospital drug centres may be open for only a few hours a week.

Some hospitals have in-patient residential withdrawal facilities but it should be said that hospitals do not, on the whole, have a very good record for getting addicts off their drugs permanently.

They all have long waiting lists and very limited catchment areas. Treatment itself varies considerably, from those who prescribe methadone to other clinics who will not consider it and who favour a City Roads type approach.

Rehabilitation Houses

These are long-term centres which aim to help users readjust to life without drugs. It is not possible for parents or friends to push addicts into these houses — the motivation must come from the user. Otherwise, it has been found, the treatment cannot work. Some rehabilitation houses are Christian-based and a conversion constitutes part of the cure. The psychoanalyst Carl Jung stated once that no healing can ever take place unless the ill person achieves a religious outlook but not all addicts, by any means, are prepared to embrace an organized religion.

Some houses are more like hostels, where the addict is offered support and guidance but no religion. Some are reward-and-punishment type set-ups, where new arrivals must earn successive privileges over a year. Referrals can come from anywhere — doctors, street agencies, City Roads — and these houses are always full to bursting.

Phoenix House, the biggest and best known of the therapeutic communities — where privileges must be earned — believe that they have a fifty per cent success rate. For many, going to Phoenix House marks the end of the addiction and the degrading purposeless lifestyle that goes with it.

Drugline

This Birmingham agency was founded by three individuals: a former addict, the mother of a user, and a probation officer. Its helpers are voluntary, but are trained in drug use and misuse. Counselling for users, and their friends or families, is available during office hours and on three evenings a week. There is also a parents' support group. Drugline has found that half their calls come from users and half from parents or other relatives. Most of the relatives who contact Drugline are mothers: they outnumber fathers by three to one. Few of their heroin users are registered and they have not previously sought treatment. Drugline also offers education, information and referral services, and has links with all the main statutory services. They are in contact with hospital Addiction Treatment Units nearby, and will refer when they feel it is appropriate.

Roma

This is a West London long-term rehabilitation house, designed for those whose lives have become completely unviable through long-term misuse of drugs. Residents are all notified drug users who are receiving prescriptions from their GP or a treatment centre. Most of the people who come to Roma are male and by far the great majority have been using drugs for many years. They will usually have attempted detoxification and rehabilitation in the past, but without much success. Nearly all have criminal records and have suffered serious physical illness from continued drug abuse.

Furthermore, most residents at Roma will normally have lost contact with their partners or spouses, and will have no sympathetic relatives at all. Any children they may have will be in care, and they have no reliable friends. When they come to Roma drug users are at crisis point, and feel they cannot go on any longer. For them, drug use will have led to a multiplication of ills: apart from being in poor physical condition and often homeless, they will have serious legal and social problems, and will not have worked for several years.

The aim at Roma is to provide accommodation, counselling, and an opportunity to lead an independent life. Residents will be helped to find jobs. Roma does not necessarily believe that all residents should become drug-free. They believe, unlike many other rehabilitation houses, that it is possible to work with addicts who are still using. They do admit, however, that it is more difficult and frustrating to work with drug users than those who are making a serious attempt to become free of their habit. Roma is now trying to encourage more women to use its facilities.

Turning Point

This is a national voluntary organization which has been in existence for about twenty years. During that time it has built up a wide range of services for both alcohol and drug problems. It has a national network of twenty-two projects, which provide a great variety of facilities. These include residential rehabilitation, (Suffolk House in Iver, Buckinghamshire, is the best known) day programmes, and advisory and counselling services.

Turning Point's work is co-ordinated in central London by a team of professional workers, and there is also a regional office in Manchester. Anybody connected with drugs — whether user, relatives, police or medical personnel — can contact Turning Point, when they will be put in touch with the appropriate help agency or treatment centre.

Suffolk House

This is a small rehabilitation house, with only fifteen beds. It is defined as a 'concept' house — a term first used in America in the 1950s — and its aim is to help addicts change or modify the behaviour that has led them to use drugs in the first place. The underlying philosophy at Suffolk House is that drugs are actually a symptom of a much deeper problem. Before the drug abuse itself can be tackled, the more fundamental problem needs to be identified and sorted out.

The regime at Suffolk House is strict and there are no soft options. Drugs are not allowed. Most residents stay for several months and rehabilitation is carried out in three phases. The first phase lasts for about a month and allows addicts to get used to a drug-free existence. The second phase tries to get to the heart of the problem; and the third phase prepares former users to socialize with others, and start thinking about getting back to work. The fourth and final phase is when a resident actually goes out to work, but is still living in the house.

An important part of the Phase Two stage is when the user writes out his life history so that attitudes and behaviour patterns learned in early childhood can be recognized. The idea behind this is to enable people to see why they have started taking drugs in the first place.

At first residents are not allowed family visits, but as they move into Phase Two these may be received on open days, which are held every six weeks.

This method of treatment is not suitable for every type of addict, but is probably of most value to the fairly young user who really wants to make an effort to lead a drug-free and useful life in future. At Suffolk House, referrals have increased tremendously in the last few years. In 1983, there was a fifty-four per cent increase over the previous year.

There is a slight emphasis on Christianity at Suffolk House, and the annual report for 1983 said that many residents were attending confirmation classes. But, unlike some houses, conversion is not insisted upon and many people do not discover a re-awakening of spiritual values. Those who are confirmed atheists would not be turned away on this account, but the scheme is possibly more suitable for those who are at least open-minded about religion and who would be prepared to change their views.

Broadway Lodge
This has been called the 'Eton of rehabilitation houses' and, as one newspaper put it, the place is just as exclusive and twice as expensive as any leading public school. Six weeks in Broadway Lodge, which is run as a charity, costs £2,400 (1985 figures).

Broadway Lodge understands that addicts experience an aching void on withdrawal, which is similar to losing a spouse. Over the years of the addiction, the drug has become an intimate friend. There is a long-lasting sense of bereavement when the drug is removed. But, of course, the difference between the death of a real-life spouse and heroin withdrawal is that the drug can always come back into the person's life. Broadway takes both alcohol and heroin addicts, as it believes the two are closely related. Many heroin addicts are also alcoholics, or become so.

The underlying philosophy at Broadway is that drug addiction is a disease, and that addicts may actually have a different biochemical make-up from other people. The Lodge believes that the user must be helped to become responsible for his or her own actions. A very high seventy per cent success rate is claimed.

Narcotics Anonymous
This organization is run on exactly the same lines as the other 'anonymous' associations, and is a non-doctor, non-drug, completely self-help society.

Originally founded thirty-three years ago in America, the British branch was formed in 1980 in Chelsea, which has the reputation of being the drug centre of London. NA, which has forty to one hundred people present at each meeting, meets every day of the week. All its organizers are former addicts, or 'cleans'. At each meeting, the organizer — there are no salaries or paid officials — asks for a moment of silence to 'remember why we are here'. This is: to stop dying and start living. The Recovery Text, also known as the Addicts' Bible, is written proof that the habit can be permanently beaten, according to members.

As with the other Anonymous organizations, the addict makes a promise to himself to stop 'just for today'. A major part of each meeting is taken up with what is known as 'doing a share'. This means giving individual accounts of experiences of drug use and withdrawal. Each person who does a share must have been clean for at least three months. NA members practise total abstinence, not just from heroin or other narcotics but from all drugs.

Anybody with a drug problem can go along to an NA meeting and identity will never be revealed. Members are asked to put their belief in a 'higher Power', to take a job and to attend meetings regularly. Their leaflets describe what addiction is *not*, as they say this is harder than defining what it *is*. Addiction is not, according to NA, freedom, but a habit that soon renders you incapable of meaningful thought or action. Addictions also serve the purpose of isolating the user from other people. They mean you can exist in your own private world. It is not, however, a nice world, but one which is sick, self-centred, and self-enclosed.

Families Anonymous

This is an organization specifically for the relatives and close friends of confirmed addicts. It is run in the belief that the spouse or relative can often unwittingly make the addiction worse by having the wrong attitude. It is often the case that, if the relatives' behaviour can improve, and their responses altered to be more positive, the addict may well start to improve as well. This is an approach which is paying dividends with alcoholics. The drink-abuse charity, ACCEPT, finds that alcohol use often sets off a Pavlovian-conditioned reflex in the observer: bad habits of both user and onlooker, interacting negatively with each other, can make the addiction take hold even more firmly. As well as this, drugs and alcohol misuse very often go hand in hand.

At FA relatives are taught how to let go of their fears and problems, and are shown how to treat the addict in order to gain maximum favourable response. Families must understand that, for the addict, life may often become apparently meaningless during recovery. Deprived of the fix, and yet not established in an alternative, better lifestyle, addicts may become extremely disorientated. Addicts are, above all, people who have ceased to function as autonomous human beings and have put themselves into a category of sub-humans, at least for the time being. At FA it is realized that the relatives often have more trouble with their emotions and reactions than the actual addict. At least addicts can blot out their worries with their daily fix — the relatives have no such solution.

Dr Lefever's Method

Another method has been pioneered by a doctor, Robert Lefever, who has run an addicts' clinic in the King's Road, Chelsea, for many years. Dr Lefever enjoys shocking people and playing devil's advocate, and he has argued more than once that heroin should be legalized and on sale in pubs and clubs. He says that philosophically there is no difference at all between the mind-altering function of heroin and that of alcohol or nicotine. We are a drug-ridden culture, he says, and turn to these substances largely because we want to gain something for nothing.

Dr Lefever tells the families of addicts who refuse to go for treatment that they should turn the addicts out into the street without a penny. He does not believe in prescribing substitute drugs and is of the opinion that the problem will never be tackled by sympathy. Time and again worried, caring parents will take the addict in and provide clothes, food and money — all of which serve to weaken resolve to kick the habit.

In order to recover, believes Dr Lefever, addicts need to be stripped of all their dignity and treated with what he terms 'harsh kindness'. He feels that this is the only way they can be made to see the error of their ways and start coming off the drug. Dr Lefever's privately-run Charter Clinic, where he sees alcoholics as well as drug addicts, is not inexpensive but he claims a seventy per cent success rate.

Naloxone Treatment

Naloxone is a drug which is currently on trial in the hope that it may be used to prevent the acute symptoms of opiate withdrawal. It is not a substitute opiate but a different type of drug that is supposed to stop the panic attacks associated with withdrawal. In its simplest terms, when heroin is taken the body's levels of adrenocorticotropic hormone (ACTH) rise. This hormone causes increased arousal. When heroin is stopped the level of ACTH stays high, resulting in panic attacks, sweats, heightened sensitivity to pain and cramps. High ACTH levels also stop the production of endogenous opiates — the endorphins — which alleviate anxiety symptoms.

The action of naloxone is to reduce ACTH levels and bring the body back to normal. It may also allow the body a chance to recover more quickly. The treatment is being developed by Colin Hendrie, a psychologist at Bradford University. Naloxone is already being used in some treatment centres for addicts who have withdrawn from heroin for six weeks. This is to prevent them from being tempted to return to the stuff. Dr Hendrie is suggesting that naloxone should be given to addicts as soon as they withdraw from heroin, to prevent the over-arousal caused by continuing high ACTH levels.

Withdrawal at Home

It is not recommended for parents to try to get their own children off a heroin habit without outside help. But, as we said earlier, drug agencies and hostels tend to be oversubscribed all the time. This is how one parent managed to get her nineteen-year-old son off his heroin habit, which was costing him £90 a week. As the son obviously had no job, he was having to shoplift and steal to support his habit.

The family were middle class and lived in a luxurious home in Merseyside. The boy's mother said:

> First of all, I asked for help from the local drug units and social services, but they were either too busy, or couldn't offer help soon enough. As my son had just been arrested for shoplifting, I felt it could go on no longer.
>
> The only answer was to get my son off heroin myself. He pleaded for one last fix. I looked at this blank-staring skeleton, completely devoid of all feelings, who was still my son and could not stop crying.
>
> By midnight he was rolling around the floor clutching his stomach, clawing at the cramp. Then came the diarrhoea, the vomiting. By 3 am, he was in unbearable agony, screaming all the time: help me, mum. We ran constant hot baths hoping that might alleviate the pain. For sixty hours it went on. Hell without break. The screams, the dreadful retching, limbs flailing, body twisted, face contorted in utter anguish.
>
> I never left his side. We took it in turns to talk to him non-stop, hoping maybe we were getting through and letting him know we were there, that we cared.
>
> It seemed like sixty years but the crisis was over. But for the next twelve weeks it was touch and go. Someone was with him every second of the day and night.

But this mother's do-it-yourself detoxification worked. The court decided to put her son on probation for the shoplifting and he managed to get a job. For nearly a year now, he has led a heroin-free life and is settled into a good job.

PART THREE

5.

ALCOHOL

Unlike heroin, which seems only to have a bad side, alcohol is capable of conjuring up diametrically opposed images. On the one hand, there is the distinguished wine connoisseur, elegantly sipping a superb vintage, while at the other end of the drinking scale is the burned-out meths drinker, wrapped in old newspapers and lying on a park bench.

Drinking alcohol is unlike many other potentially addictive forms of behaviour in that it has its distinctly appealing, good-life side and about ninety per cent of those who indulge in an occasional drink will never become addicted. Yet even so, the numbers of those who are seriously addicted to alcohol remain frighteningly high. It is estimated by ACCEPT (Addictions Community Centres for Education, Prevention and Treatment) that about 750,000 people in this country are seriously dependent on alcohol, while another 650,000 or so have a definite drinking problem. The number of people entering mental hospitals each year with a drinking problem more than doubled between 1965 and 1975, and it is estimated that the cost of working days lost as a result of alcoholism is between £100 million and £500 million a year. In 1983, £15 billion was spent on alcohol — more than on leisure, fuel, books or holidays. In fact, 38p in every leisure £1 is now spent on alcohol.

It is also estimated that alcohol abuse costs the NHS about £1,000 million in England and Wales. According to some reports, about 5,000 people a year in this country could be dying prematurely from the effects of alcohol. In addition, around 20,000 people a year are admitted to psychiatric hospitals for problems directly related to drinking.

In Britain, at least, we are rapidly becoming a nation of drinkers. During the past twenty years we have doubled our intake of beer, tripled our intake of spirits, and we now drink five times more wine than in 1933. It is a sobering thought that in the five years between 1971 and 1976 convictions for drunken drivers doubled. In 1981, £100 million was spent on advertising alcohol and in 1982, £4,700 million was raised by the government through alcohol taxation. There are signs that people are starting to drink at an ever-younger age, and that more and more women are also taking to drink. At least thirty per cent of girls aged fifteen have been drunk more than once, according to a study carried out by ACCEPT, who also discovered that more than eighty per cent of boys aged sixteen, and sixty per cent of girls of the same age, have tried alcohol.

What Alcohol Does to the System

Alcohol is classified as a drug of relatively mild addiction potential. This means that most people who try it will never become addicted and in this sense it is very different from heroin, cocaine or nicotine, all of which have a very high addiction potential. The effect that alcohol has on any one person depends on their age, sex, size and how tolerant they have become to it.

If you are an eleven-stone man, or a nine-stone woman, used to a certain amount of regular drink, this is what you can expect to happen when you drink, in order: first of all, there will be an enhanced sense of well-being, but this relaxed feeling means that reaction times become reduced. This is the effect you can expect from two units of alcohol — a pint of beer, two sherries, a double whisky, or a large glass of wine.

After four units there will be a certain loss of inhibition, with impaired judgement. But at this stage there will not usually be recognizable signs of drunkenness. After five units, however, the first signs of intoxication become apparent. There will now be definite loss of co-ordination and clumsiness; there is also a noticeable lack of inhibition, and you will be well over the legal limit for driving. After seven units, loss of physical control and clumsiness will be very apparent; and after ten units, speech will become slurred and incoherent. There will be loss of short-term memory. After twenty-four units for a man and fourteen for a woman there will be possible loss of consciousness. Any man who has taken in thirty-three units, or a woman who has had twenty units, will risk the possibility of death.

The active ingredient in alcoholic drinks is ethyl alcohol and it is this that causes changes in mood and behaviour. The alcohol is absorbed from the stomach and intestines into the bloodstream and has the immediate effect of depressing the central nervous system. Many people regard alcohol as a stimulant but, in fact, it is a depressant. Although it helps people to lose their inhibitions it dulls the brain and lowers critical faculties.

Once alcohol enters the bloodstream it circulates throughout the entire body, from the brain to the toe. No part of the system is left unaffected. Alcohol will be absorbed into the bloodstream more slowly if you have just eaten, or if you eat while you continue to drink, although it will still enter all of the bloodstream eventually. Bubbly or very diluted drinks enter the bloodstream more quickly than the concentrated ones. This is why people can be taken by surprise when they drink champagne, finding they are tipsy almost at once.

The organ which has the responsibility of ridding alcohol from the system is the liver. This is done by changing the chemical composition of the alcohol so that it is available to the body as energy. But the liver can only process the equivalent of about one unit of alcohol per hour — that is, a single whisky, half a pint of beer, or a small sherry — and this is mainly why people quickly get drunk when they drink too much. If you drink three or more units an hour, most of the alcohol will be unprocessed and will remain in the blood. But if you drink slowly, say three units over three hours, your liver will very probably be able to cope quite happily and without ill-effects.

The alcohol that is processed by the liver does people no harm: it is the unprocessed stuff left over that causes damage. Firstly judgement and self-control are lost, as the alcohol is affecting brain function. This is the familiar 'drowning your sorrows'. Alcohol does make people temporarily forget their worries because it depresses certain functions in the brain. But, of course, the worries return when the alcohol effect is no longer there. The sorrows are not actually drowned, they are merely blanketed out for a short time.

Alcohol in the bloodstream also affects a number of other bodily functions. It speeds up the heart-rate and enlarges the blood vessels on the surface of the skin, causing the well-known alcoholic flush. It also stimulates the gastric juices, making you feel hungry. As it is being expelled by the body as quickly as possible, in an attempt to rid the system of harmful effects, alcohol also causes dehydration.

Many people have a drink to warm them up in cold weather.

In fact, alcohol does not really warm people up at all. What happens is that when the blood vessels on the skin's surface become enlarged, you lose warmth from the body and so become even colder. The more alcohol you drink, the more body heat is lost.

But alcohol is not all bad. A moderate amount can even have some medicinal qualities. A report in *The Lancet* in 1981 showed that, of 1,422 men studied, those who were moderate drinkers had lower mortality rates than either heavy drinkers or total abstainers. From this study it appears that only wine conveyed this protective effect, although a small whisky or brandy certainly does appear to help people suffering from shock.

Alcohol is a time-honoured painkiller and in the days before anaesthetics it was given to those facing surgery or amputation. Its painkilling properties work in a similar way to heroin: the pain is not actually killed, but the brain's perception of physical hurt is damped down. In the same way, alcohol can blot out mental pain for a time.

There is some evidence that patients in hospital who are allowed a small glass of wine or sherry each day recover more quickly than those who drink nothing. When the spirits are lifted mentally, the body is often encouraged to respond positively as well. It could be that the feeling of mild well-being which moderate amounts of alcohol encourage makes the body actually start getting physically well again.

The Effects of Heavy Drinking

Heavy drinking, however, does nobody any good, least of all the drinker. In purely social terms alcohol brings out the less likeable sides of the personality. Drunkenness increases the chances of having an accident, getting into a row, or behaving foolishly. It destroys relationships, but also has a very far-reaching effect on many bodily conditions. In a number of ways alcohol can increase chances of succumbing to serious illness.

The commonest physical side-effect of heavy drinking is liver damage. Persistent heavy drinking can cause liver cells to die and be replaced with fibrous tissue: this is the condition known as cirrhosis of the liver, which can lead to death. But this serious condition is not the only adverse effect on the liver. After a few days of continuous drinking the liver becomes enlarged. It is a very long-suffering organ, however, and if drinking is only occasional, it will right itself long before the next bout. It is the continuous onslaught that destroys liver function.

Almost all heavy drinkers are overweight. This happens because they consume more calories in the form of alcohol than they can use, so the excess is stored as fat. Vitamin deficiency can also occur, for two reasons: one is that many drinkers consume alcohol rather than nutritious food; but, also, alcohol has the effect of leaching valuable vitamins and minerals out of the system.

Steady drinking, maintained daily over a number of years, can cause high blood-pressure and heart conditions. Heart muscle can also be weakened by the extra effort of having to pump ethyl alcohol round the system. The blood can become overloaded and the heart unable to pump efficiently. Too much alcohol can have an adverse effect on the brain, reducing its size and intelligence. Tests on heavy drinkers have shown that they become less intelligent than non-drinkers eventually.

Another main adverse effect is that stomach ulcers and irritation can result, caused by too many gastric juices being produced in response to the alcohol. Certain cancers, of the liver, mouth and throat are also associated with too much alcohol, although they may not be a direct result. The older a person is the greater the likelihood that some, or all, of these diseases will eventually result. Younger people's systems can take more alcoholic punishment but, as a general rule, the smaller and thinner you are, the greater and sooner the damage.

Many people who drink usually indulge in a good deal of self-deception. A study undertaken by *Which?* magazine found that at least three out of ten people underestimate their alcohol consumption and those who describe themselves as 'moderate' drinkers may be considered heavy drinkers by a more objective assessor.

The Health Education Council has set down what it considers to be light, moderate, and heavy drinking levels. A man who drinks less than twenty units of alcohol a week, or ten pints of beer, or a woman drinking thirteen units or less a week, are unlikely to be damaging their health. Light drinking is defined as nought to ten units a week, whereas very heavy drinking would be forty-five to fifty units a week for a man, thirty-five units or more for a woman.

However long you have been drinking, and however bad your liver or insides generally, there is always a good chance that, if you stop drinking, these conditions can be reversed or improved. But it is becoming known now that alcohol has a far more damaging effect on women than it has on men, both for themselves and for any children they may have.

Alcohol and Women

Women's bodies are not designed by nature to be able to cope with large amounts of alcohol and damage sets in far sooner than it does with men. Any woman who drinks more than four units a day will eventually have an alcohol-related health problem. Women's bodies are smaller than men's and have a higher proportion of body fat, which does not absorb alcohol. This means that, for a woman, alcohol is in her body in a more concentrated form.

There is no doubt that women are now drinking more as they are increasingly going into the outside world and ACCEPT are now dealing with one hundred new cases of female alcoholism per month. In fact the majority of female dependent drinkers are far more likely to be outwardly successful professional people than seemingly hopeless depressives. Inwardly, though, they may be plagued by low self-esteem and not absolutely sure how best to conduct themselves in the world at large. Women in most danger of becoming dependent drinkers are those who are not naturally self-assertive but who would like to be. They may also be prey to constant feelings of anxiety, frustration, loneliness and boredom. Very often they will have been conditioned to defer to, please and placate men at the expense of their own self-fulfilment and development. Women very often feel that their own deep needs are not being met and that they are just living to please others; eventually, this can result in them not knowing quite who they are. Alcohol can then be used as a way of helping women to get back in touch with themselves, at this very intimate level.

DAWN (Drugs, Alcohol, Women, Nationally) is an organization that researches into the reasons why women turn to drink and drugs, and puts them in touch with women-oriented help associations. In its booklet, *Women and Drinking,* it has this to say on the subject:

> When we can't manage without something in our everyday lives, we say we're dependent on it. There are many different ways of being dependent on many different things. Because of the values of our society, women are encouraged to be dependent in some ways but not in others. It's okay, for instance, to be dependent on a man: in

fact, it's expected. It's usually okay to be dependent on sugar or coffee, or even cigarettes. Dependency is only seen as a bad thing in women when it interferes with our roles — as housewife, mother or worker.

Often women start using drugs as a way of coping with the demands of these roles — a pill to relax us before a meeting, a drink to pep us up before the shopping. As women, we're trained to meet the needs of others before our own. That's why the reasons women are given for not using drugs are usually to do with our servicing others — don't smoke for your baby's sake, don't drink for your husband's, and so on. Taking drugs can be an attempt to meet our needs . . . Women are brought up to look after other people's feelings, not our own. We may try to use alcohol to blot out our feelings, particularly the unfeminine ones like anger, frustration or power.

Charles Vetter, the American founder of ACCEPT, has said: 'The more comfortable you are, the less likely you are to need to escape by using alcohol or drugs.'

ACCEPT have pinpointed several danger signals specially for women, to enable them to tell whether they may be in any danger from alcohol. According to them, you may have a potential drinking problem if: you tend to gulp your drinks rather than sip them; you feel the need to have a drink *before* going to a party, or other gathering where there will be plenty of drink available; you feel the need to have a drink at certain times of the day; you insist that there should be enough time for a few drinks before dinner; you must have a drink before any special or out of the ordinary event; you absolutely must have a drink when either your own or your husband's boss is coming for dinner; you take a drink to calm your nerves, or to drown your worries.

In general, the more successful and useful you feel you are, the less you will need a drink. Enjoying one is a different matter, but there should always be cause for alarm, ACCEPT says, when you feel you are incapable of enjoying any social occasion without some alcohol.

From a health point of view, there may be many dangers for women. The alcohol that circulates around the body is distributed throughout the body's fluids. In men, this is between fifty-five and sixty-five per cent of the body, but in women, these fluids make up only forty-five to fifty-five per cent. Women also have smaller livers so damage can result at a lower level of drinking than would be safe for men.

There can also be considerable damage to an unborn baby. The Foetal Alcohol Syndrome, where unborn babies are adversely affected by their mothers' drinking, has now been recognized as an actual condition. A pioneering study on the subject, reported in the *British Journal of Hospital Medicine* in 1983, showed that a woman who drinks a bottle of wine or more a day, is vastly increasing her chances of having an abnormal baby. A large-scale study of mothers in Boston in 1977 found that thirty-two per cent of handicapped infants were born to heavy drinking mothers, fourteen per cent to moderate drinkers and nine per cent to total abstainers. Such is the evidence that women who wish to become pregnant are now advised to give up drinking altogether before they even conceive. At the moment, about twenty-six per cent of pregnant women still have the occasional drink.

The effect of alcohol on a developing baby is great simply because the new life is so small. Recent research says that the birth weight of a baby might be reduced if its mother has an alcohol intake of even ten units a week. There is not a safe alcohol limit for pregnant women, as individual differences rule this out. But the main recommendation from experts is that preferably alcohol should be cut out completely during pregnancy. Further, it is a good idea to stop alcohol before pregnancy is confirmed, as the greatest damage may be done in the early stages of a developing life. Two drinks a week have been associated with an increased miscarriage rate, but at this level there would be little harm to the unborn child.

The Foetal Alcohol Syndrome is a condition that results from very heavy drinking, but this does not need to be consistently maintained for there to be an effect. Babies can be affected when mothers go on drinking binges during pregnancy; a 'binge' at this time being defined as five units or more. A Foetal Alcohol Syndrome (FAS) baby is born with facial and physical deformities and is usually mentally retarded. As it grows up development and general growth will be slower than normal, and it is likely to be affected in some way all its life.

Alcohol and Teenagers
More teenagers than ever before are becoming drink-dependent. Even before the age of twenty these days you are considered odd if you don't want to drink, and there is a lot of pressure on young people to consume alcohol from a very early age indeed. Some schools now allow sixth-formers to drink wine on special occasions and it is not uncommon for teenagers of fifteen or sixteen to be offered drink in their parents' or relatives' houses.

There is nothing necessarily wrong in this, except that it can establish the drinking habit at an early age and make alcohol seem a normal, even necessary, adjunct to adult life.

During the teens and early twenties, it is more likely to be males who are drinking heavily. Professor Dame Sheila Sherlock, of the Royal Free Hospital, London, stated in a report published in *The Lancet* that most men who drink heavily are hardly eating at all, but are deriving around 3,300 calories a day in 'empty' form from their alcohol. She said that a degree of alcoholism should always be suspected in an overweight young man, especially if he has a noticeable pot belly.

The problem has grown so much in recent years that thousands of children are now actually needing hospital treatment for drink-related problems. Geoffrey Hepburn, director of the Greater London Alcohol Advisory Service, said recently that it is extremely easy for young people to obtain alcohol and that most young people learn about drinking from their parents. In a report published early in 1985 by the Advisory Service, it was stated that children under fifteen years of age now account for ten per cent of hospital admissions for drink problems in one part of Essex. This picture is now reflected round the country.

The best way for parents to alert children to the dangers of alcohol is to sit down and explain everything to them in a cool and calm way. Parents and teachers should point out that, although drink can be a valuable social lubricant, and enjoyable, there is also a dangerous negative side. Young people should not, under any circumstances, drink alone or when feeling miserable. Alcohol should be kept strictly within a social context.

There are also ways of drinking that will minimize any risk and maximize enjoyment. Many young people who are new to drinking gulp, rather than sip. They drink wine as if it were lemonade. So it is important to point out that anything alcoholic should be treated with extreme caution and sipped very slowly. An alcoholic drink should be alternated with a non-alcoholic one at a party. Youngsters often do not have any knowledge of sensible pub and party behaviour, or the different effects of different drinks. Some may imagine that being able to hold vast amounts of drink is a sign of being grown up, and that the more you are able to drink the more grown up you are. But real maturity means acquiring the knowledge of sensible drinking.

As with any drug, the best thing any parent can do is to provide a good example. It has been shown in several surveys that the

teenagers who are most likely to turn to drink are those who come
from homes where drunkenness is normal behaviour. Either that,
or they live with adults who are dedicated total abstainers and
who talk endlessly about the evils of drink. To provide a good
example, parents do not have to abstain from all alcohol
themselves but show that wine, beer and spirits can be drunk
enjoyably in a social context, without anybody getting hangovers
or being ill afterwards.

What to Do if There's a Drink Problem

If you feel that you, or a member of your family, or a close friend,
are in danger of developing a drink problem, the issue should
not be ignored. That way, it can only get worse. There is now
a great deal of help available and it should be remembered that
many people who are dependent drinkers, or who are liable to
become so, do need skilled, professional help. Once alcohol has
become an addiction, or a way of life, it can be difficult to break
the habit on one's own.

The first step lies in establishing how dangerous the drinking
has become and how great its hold now is on the person
concerned. For those who are not yet addicted, but who are
finding it increasingly difficult to get through a single day without
alcohol, *Drinkwatchers,* which exists to teach people how to drink
sensibly and moderately, may be the answer.

Only a very few people who have become completely
dependent on alcohol can ever return to occasional drinking; for
the majority total lifelong abstinence must be the aim. The merest
taste of alcohol could cause the habit to be re-established, as many
alcoholics have found to their cost. For people in this position,
Alcoholics Anonymous, ACCEPT or a drying-out period as an
in-patient in hospital would be needed.

It can be very hard indeed for a relative to suggest that a drinker
might join AA or ACCEPT, as this very suggestion is often
interpreted as hostile criticism and may even make the problem
worse. So anybody who is genuinely worried that their husband,
wife, child or parent is drinking excessively, should first ask the
family doctor to have a word. If that would not be a good solution,
perhaps the boss at work, or an objective friend, might raise the
subject tactfully. It can be a good idea to ask somebody who
themselves has already managed to overcome their own serious
drinking problem to talk to the drinker. It has to be borne in mind
that drinkers are already feeling very defensive and guilty about

their habit and have to be handled with care. If they were coping with their problems in a logical way they wouldn't be drinking in the first place. Anybody who is drinking excessively is suffering from an illness which is both mental and physical, and great diplomacy and tact is needed to help them reverse all the bad behaviour associated with drinking.

The following is a brief outline of the main kinds of drink-abuse help now available in Britain.

Drinkwatchers

This is the only help group that emphasizes sensible controlled drinking rather than total abstinence, and it is aimed at those whose drinking has not yet got out of hand. Drinkwatchers was set up by ACCEPT and is for those at the halfway stage.

The groups are intended for young people who are just starting to drink, as well as men and women who are afraid that their alcohol intake is escalating to an undesirable level. Drinkwatcher groups are now established in many parts of the country and were founded in 1982 as a national network of self-help groups. They are not recommended for people who are already harmfully dependent on alcohol, or whose health has suffered seriously as a result of drinking. The groups are designed to stop addictions before they take hold.

When people join Drinkwatchers they are choosing to learn how to drink differently, rather than giving up all alcohol. This means a daily maximum of six units for men and four for women. Among the sensible drinking tips recommended by Drinkwatchers are: first of all, drink slowly. Don't finish your drink before other people finish theirs. Order half pints rather than pints, or single measures rather than doubles. Dilute spirits rather than drinking them neat. Always alternate alcoholic with non-alcoholic drinks and make the first drink of the evening a non-alcoholic one, particularly if you are thirsty. Set specific time limits for each glass to be emptied and don't cheat on this. Decide on your upper limit before you go out drinking for the evening. Eat while you drink and try never to drink on an empty stomach. At home, always keep a supply of non-alcoholic drinks and don't stockpile booze.

On an emotional level, you must try to resist the urge to drink when you feel physical or mental tension or irritability. Drinkwatcher groups are aware that a certain number of withdrawal symptoms will be experienced for those who have come to rely on daily drinks. These will be felt as tension, irritability, sweatiness, or a dry mouth. But these feelings will pass and become less intense in a very short time. As you are able to resist drinks you will become more self-confident and strong in yourself.

Drinkwatchers also advise people to take up rewarding and enjoyable activities, as things to do instead of drinking. Suggested activities include: swimming, dancing, jogging, keep fit and walking. Relaxing pastimes are yoga, saunas, massage, relaxation classes and meditation. All these will help to keep your mind off drink and will make you feel better at the same time.

Alcoholics Anonymous

This, the best known and the first of the 'Anonymous' organizations, was founded in 1935 in America by a New York stockbroker and an Ohio surgeon. AA arrived in Britain in 1947 and now has over one million members in 104 countries. The members are all people with drinking problems and the organization is completely self-help in type. As its aims and procedures are so similar to Narcotics Anonymous, described in detail on page 73, and Gamblers, Anonymous, only a brief outline is given here.

Anybody who has a drinking problem can go along to an AA meeting, or be referred by a doctor or hospital. The emphasis is on total abstention for the rest of the person's life. Meetings consist of stories told by former alcoholics who have now managed to control their drinking; some of these are truly horrific. Members are given one year, five year and ten year badges, as in the other Anonymous organizations.

There is a twelve-point recovery plan and members are asked to put their trust in a higher power. The programme is designed to help members feel more confident in themselves, to have better self-esteem, and to rely on their innate coping skills, so that they will not turn to alcohol in times of crisis.

Very often, it can be almost as bad to live with an alcoholic as to be one and AA has set up special Al-Anon and Alateen groups for the relatives and children of alcoholics. Advice is given on how to handle members of the family who have developed a drinking problem and how to alter their own attitudes, so they are helpful and sympathetic rather than condemnatory.

Almost all of the Anonymous organizations have a strong

religious flavour. Some people find this extremely helpful and comforting, while others discover that such an approach is not for them. For such people the newer, rather different methods of ACCEPT might be more suitable.

ACCEPT

This is a voluntary organization founded by Charles Vetter about ten years ago. Since then it has revolutionized approaches to drinking problems in this country. Not the least of these is the decision to drop the word 'alcoholic' which was preventing many people from seeking treatment. Charles Vetter said: 'We were getting a lot of referrals from people who said, "I've got a drinking problem but I'm not alcoholic." The word itself is very offputting.' Charles Vetter calls ACCEPT's approach 'cool and scientific' and the main idea is to deal with the underlying problem, the reason for drinking, rather than the drinking itself. ACCEPT sees problem drinking as a symptom, rather than a disorder in its own right.

Clients are never referred to as alcoholics, unlike at AA where they are constantly reminded of the fact, and they can come by themselves, be referred by doctors or hospitals, or be put in touch by their firms. When a new client comes to ACCEPT, the first task is to discover just how serious the drinking problem is and to check whether the client has seen his doctor or been to hospital already. They recommend that clients should keep in touch with doctors, as health may have to be very carefully monitored. Sometimes a course of Valium, or similar drug, may be needed to help with the worst of the withdrawal symptoms, which may include shakes, sweats and anxiety attacks.

As with heroin addiction, the worst of the physical effects wear off in just a few days, but finding another way to cope with the problem that caused over-drinking in the first place is far more difficult. Usually, there will be many problems which have been masked by the drinking: the client may be having trouble at work, be unemployed, or generally feeling a failure in life.

At first a new client must attend ACCEPT meetings every day for two weeks. The doctor will be contacted and requested to give a sick note. If the firm does not know about the drinking problem, or would be shocked at the knowledge, euphemistic wording may be required. ACCEPT will help with this as well.

ACCEPT finds that most clients must abstain totally from alcohol for the rest of their lives. Only a very, very small proportion will ever be able to return to social drinking. Usually, dependent drinkers do not seek help, or are not recommended for it, until the drinking has become a very serious condition indeed. The few who may be able to return to occasional drinking later are those whose drinking has been caused by a single stress-related episode, such as bereavement or redundancy. But ACCEPT points out that people who can do this are in a very tiny minority. For the most part, the aim is 'positive non-drinking' for the rest of the client's life. The eventual aim is also independence from any drink-abuse agency.

When the client comes to ACCEPT he or she will be able to take part in a wide range of activities, from yoga and art to assertiveness training and job-finding classes. The idea is to find one that suits the client individually. The most popular courses are on self-assertion. This is because people most often start drinking when they realize that they are basically very passive types who allow themselves to be put upon. Drinking makes them more aggressive, yet underneath the resentments and frustrations remain. People's characters are never really altered for the better by drink. Assertiveness courses teach clients how to set about getting their rights and making their views known in a calm and controlled way. In some cases clients may be suffering from quite severe psychiatric problems which have been masked by the drinking. But these make up only perhaps ten per cent of the total clients.

Nearly all dependent drinkers will never again be able to drink successfully. Any compromise eventually leads to heavy drinking again, as both AA and ACCEPT have found. The aim has to be to break all links with the previous habit.

Although AA and ACCEPT are both very successful they each have quite a high proportion of failures and backsliders. But all of AA's members and most of the founders and executives of ACCEPT have themselves suffered from a serious drinking problem in the past, so they do know how difficult it can be to break the habit.

Alcohol Dependency Units

There are about twenty-six of these and a referral from a GP is needed. There is at least one dependency unit in every regional health authority, and a total of around 700 beds. There is always a very long list of people waiting for admission and treatment, which lasts from three weeks to about three months. An important aspect of the recovery programme is group therapy sessions, which are proving popular and effective.

Alcohol Recovery Project

This has worked with male homeless alcoholics for the past nineteen years and it has now opened its doors to women as well. The residential facilities are mixed, and each house can accommodate from six to ten people.

No drinking at all is allowed in these houses, which are charitably run, and usually the people who arrive for treatment are those who have tried everything without success. Their lives have become completely chaotic and their health is poor as a direct result of over-drinking. The clients will typically have lost their families and friends, become guilty, despairing, suicidal, and have lost all vestiges of self-respect. It has been found that women tend to experience greater loss of self-esteem than male residents. The basic question all residents must face is: am I worth getting sober for?

There must be a positive answer to this, otherwise the likelihood of recovery is small. When people first come to ARP houses they will be accepted as they are. Often just stepping over the threshold is the first stage on the road to recovery. All the residents know that they are among people whose problems are identical to their own, and this in itself can give a sense of comfort. There is no longer any need to lie or cheat or deceive, or to try and cover up the drinking, as there may have been in other situations. In these homes there is no recrimination over drinking or over a misspent past. That is all forgotten, as everybody looks to a drink-free future.

The homes have found that women alcoholics particularly need to become independent, not just from the drink, but also from other people, and they have to learn that it is not a solution to hope to find a decent man. Women tend to do better in women-only groups the Project has found, as they relate more to each other and become more talkative than in mixed groups.

Drug treatment

There are one or two drugs available which will reverse, to a certain extent, the effects of alcohol in the body, or will sensitize the system to alcohol.

Antabuse is one drug which can be prescribed by the doctor and some people running alcohol dependency units swear by it. Dr Colin Brewer, director of the Community Alcohol Treatment

Unit at Westminster Hospital, believes these alcohol-sensitizing drugs can be very useful indeed in helping compulsive drinkers. The biggest problem that doctors have with Antabuse is to persuade drinkers to take the tablets, as they make alcohol taste very nasty indeed. One solution here is to ask the drinker's spouse, or a relative, to dissolve the tablets in water first and then give them to the alcoholic. Dr Brewer feels that, though this method treats the symptoms rather than the underlying cause, it can still be very successful. He can quote many examples of clients who have dropped out of AA meetings and yet managed to kick the habit with a course of Antabuse.

A sobering-up pill called Sober Aid, supposed to reverse the effects of drinking instantly, for drivers and the like, is now being tested in America. It is a 'cocktail' of vitamins — to counteract vitamin deficiency associated with a chronic alcohol consumption, fructose — to speed up elimination of alcohol, and a clay-like substance that absorbs alcohol in the gut. It is said to reduce intoxification by forty per cent.

Private treatments
There are also many private clinics which offer drying-out cures, but these cost many hundreds of pounds a week. A list is available from SCODA, the Standing Conference on Drug Abuse. The techniques in private clinics are very similar to those used by NHS Dependency Units, and the rate of success about the same.

How to tell if you (or somebody close to you) may have a drinking problem
If you can answer yes to two or more of these questions, there may well be a problem over drink:

- Do you need to drink to give you confidence? Do you need to drink *before* going to a party?
- Do you drink when you are alone, particularly when you are depressed, miserable or worried?
- Do you find you are drinking earlier and earlier in the day?
- Do you find you down your drinks very quickly and always finish before other people?
- Do you order yourself a double when the rest of the group are drinking singles?
- Do you order two bottles of wine in a restaurant when there are just two or three of you present?

More serious danger signs are:

- If you feel increasingly that you no longer have any control over your drinking.
- If you can no longer take it or leave it.
- You feel a sense of shame when you remember your behaviour after a drinking session.
- You have to take time off work because of over-drinking.
- Your work performance has suffered as a result of drinking.
- You conceal from those around you the amount you drink.
- Your memory is getting worse after drinking.
- Your sexual drive and ability has suffered as a result of drinking.

If you can answer yes to *any* of these, then help should be sought without delay.

6.

GAMBLING

In previous chapters, we have seen how teenagers and young people are becoming seriously addicted to illegal drugs and alcohol, both of which are constituting a rapidly growing problem. To these two activities now has to be added a third: gambling.

Teenage Gambling

Many more teenagers than ever before are now becoming gambling addicts, haunting fruit machine arcades and space invader machines, mesmerized by the flashing lights and the hope of the ever-elusive jackpot or 'high score'. Dr Emmanuel Moran, consultant psychiatrist at Enfield District Hospital, has discovered that about two-thirds of London schools now face gambling problems, and many pupils have developed serious addictions. Alan Baldwin, a youth worker with the Soho Project, holds the view that young teenage gambling is a growing national problem.

Fruit machines are a definite attraction — some would say menace — to modern youth, and their numbers have increased by forty per cent in the past ten years. At one time confined to seaside arcades, they are now finding their way into cafés, pubs and clubs. They attract mainly boys; very few girls find themselves irresistibly drawn to them. The reason for this is not hard to find. Boys, more than girls, love to feel they have power over things, that inanimate objects are within their control. They also find it harder than girls to form proper relationships in the teenage years. This can lead to them succumbing to obsessive forms of behaviour, such as twenty-four hour computer programming and all night fruit machine gambling. For many boys this compulsion lasts only a short time and as soon as they have jobs, girlfriends, or otherwise grow up, the addiction will vanish. But for a seriously growing number, the addiction will grow and grow until it replaces all other activities. Two stories will illustrate how fruit machine gambling can take hold in very young people.

Nigel left school at sixteen and found work in an office. His addiction started, he said, at the same time as he started work and, for the first time in his life, had money to jangle in his pocket. He said:

> Where I live, in North London, there aren't many fruit machines, so it wasn't a problem. But coming up to work in the centre of the city, I found they were all around me. I suppose I felt lonely, and I didn't have many friends, so they became my friends and social life.
>
> Before long, I was hanging out in arcades in every spare minute and was gambling every single day. Soon, I was gambling all I earned and more. I borrowed money, and it soon developed into an addiction I simply couldn't break. It's ridiculous, really, when you consider that the most you can win on a fruit machine is £2 in tokens.
>
> What excited me wasn't so much the actual winning, but the noises, the lights, the fruits flashing by, the hold button and the nudges. Whenever I won the jackpot, I put all my money straight back, and was never satisfied until I had gambled my last 10p.
>
> The length of time I played depended on how long the money lasted, but two hours at a time was not unusual. I lost all my friends, as I thought about nothing but gambling. I couldn't afford to go out, as I needed everything I could get to gamble. It was exactly like taking a drug, I needed the 'high' to escape from reality.

Nigel, who has now managed to kick the habit, says: 'I think a lot of teenagers who gamble are essentially shy, insecure people. When you are on a fruit machine, you can avoid talking, and human contact, and you can forget yourself for a time. But by the end, I was putting £100 a week into the machine. As I was earning £80, finding money to finance the habit became a major problem and I was in dreadful debt. I had already resorted to stealing.'

Paul started gambling compulsively at the age of fourteen. He said:

> By the age of eighteen, I was spending two-thirds of my time gambling, and the other third thinking about it. When I wasn't actually in an arcade, I was thinking about how I could win the jackpot.
>
> By 16, I was already spending half my income on fruit machines. I worked near King's Cross, where there is an amusement arcade,

and that really established the gambling habit for me. I got into very bad trouble eventually, and owed everywhere. There was no possible way of paying back what I owed, so I either had to win, or steal it.

The attraction, for Paul, of fruit machines was the feeling of coming alive as play was in progress. 'You're never satisfied until you have lost everything,' he said. 'When you do win, you subconsciously feel you are not entitled to the money, and you have to put it back. You actually enjoy yourself when you are losing. It's difficult to explain the attraction exactly, but somehow you feel good when you have lost. After a few hours, the urge to lose more money comes back.

'I know many young people who were as hooked as me. Most of them start when they are fourteen or fifteen, and they are all boys. I've never met a girl who was hooked on fruit machines.'

Fortunately, Nigel and Paul found their salvation at junior branches of Gamblers' Anonymous, the only self-help organization in this country devoted to helping gamblers and their families.

Why Gamble?

Why do people gamble to excess? Gamblers' Anonymous, which began in this country in 1964, has analysed the problem. There are around 100,000 compulsive gamblers in Britain and the GA view is that these are people in the grip of a progressive illness.

Firstly, people are attracted to gambling when they are unable or unwilling to accept reality as they find it. This means they are easily lured into the dream world of placing bets and hoping for a win. If they are ever to have a hope of accepting reality they first must genuinely want to stop gambling. As with other types of addicts, not all will want to obtain release from their addiction and many continue to feel that gambling is the only thing that gives their life meaning. This is why compulsive gamblers, in common with other addicts, very often return to their habit at times of crisis, or when their will weakens. It seems as if gambling, which is exciting and stimulating in itself, can be a way of evading deeper personal problems. Underneath, however, the problems don't just remain, but actually become more unsolvable. In time, there is not only the underlying problem that caused the gambling, but also the very considerable anguish resulting from the compulsion to lose money.

Gamblers are very often people who suffer emotional

insecurity. Many feel at ease only when they are actually gambling. They are people who want to have the good things in life without any great personal effort. Subconsciously, many gamblers feel they can avoid facing up to adult responsibilities by risking all on the spin of a wheel or the position of a horse. Eventually, as the addiction takes an ever-stronger hold, the actual struggle to escape from any responsibility at all becomes an obsession in itself.

GA also feels that most compulsive gamblers have an inner urge to be a 'big shot' and all-powerful. In some sense, the nightly wager with the roulette wheel or black jack is just like being engaged in battle. The major difference is that, with gambling, defeat is absolutely guaranteed.

The final theory propounded by GA is that many compulsive gamblers are masochists and secretly want to punish themselves. At any rate, all gamblers come to live in a world that is far removed from any kind of reality. They conjure up images of all the wonderful things they will do with their winnings — the good life, complete with yacht, swimming pool, world tours, donations to charity and so on, is always only just around the corner. The reality, of course, is that there never ever is a big win. Even when a substantial sum may be accrued from a successful night's gaming, it will certainly be lost, and more, the following night.

In order to relinquish the addiction, gamblers must work to bring about a positive personality transformation within themselves. As with all other compulsions, nobody but the gambler can decide when he has had enough. His own personal rock bottom has to be reached before he will seek help. GA do not believe that the addiction can ever be cured by abolishing gambling, which is, in any case, virtually impossible to outlaw completely. In Thailand, for example, gambling is actually illegal, yet it is virtually the national sport.

Many doctors believe that compulsive gamblers are severely depressed people. Dr Richard A. McCormick, a psychologist from Cleveland, USA, has found that a very high percentage of patients he sees for gambling compulsion are also suffering from very bad depression.

How Gambling Sets In

Dr Ivor Phillips, a GP and medical adviser to GA believes that one of the biggest problems with gambling is that the last person to admit to an addiction is the gambler himself. As with other addictions gambling brings about an adverse personality transformation, so that what may be clear to others cannot be seen by the gambler.

Dr Phillips says that the pattern of compulsive gambling always follows the same course, whether it originates from the humble fruit machine or the big-style punter at race meetings. In a very high proportion of cases there will be a gambling background and participation will begin at an extremely early age, usually starting with tossing pennies up the wall or seeing which fly goes up the window first.

Often by the early teens gambling will already have become a way of life and all spare time and money be devoted to it. Money is forever in short supply because no compulsive gambler can ever hope to win, for two main reasons. One is that it is impossible to beat the odds, however brilliant the 'system' may be, or however mathematically exact it may be in principle. The second reason is that, by definition, the compulsive gambler cannot stop gambling, whether he is winning or losing. He lives in a dream world of having one big win which will launch him into a world of affluence. This dream can never come true because when there is a big win, which does happen sometimes, it only provides more money to sustain the addiction.

The lives of everybody connected with a gambler inevitably suffer. Physically, the gambler's health will deteriorate and he will show signs of years of stress. Depression, anxiety, peptic ulcers, angina, even attempted suicide, will all be the lot of the addicted gambler. Gambling takes an immense toll on physical health, a factor that not everybody realizes.

Compulsive gamblers must usually seek some form of outside help for their gambling, as they will forever be living on a knife edge. In future, they dare not risk buying even a raffle ticket — in case the urge comes back. Total abstention, as with alcoholism, is the only effective answer.

Case Histories

Anybody attending a meeting of Gamblers' Anonymous will be in for something of a surprise. Instead of seeing a bunch of seedy, down and out, defeated-looking people, the onlooker will view instead rows and rows of smartly dressed, successful-looking individuals. For the truth is that many gamblers are intelligent, effective businesspeople who are good at making money. In many cases, those who have lost fortunes through gambling will be able to build them up again once the compulsion is under control.

At a GA meeting members take it in turns to tell their stories, always starting with the words: 'I am a compulsive gambler' for GA believes that once a gambler, always a gambler, and members must constantly be reminded of the fact. As with the other Anonymous organizations, GA truly is anonymous and surnames are never revealed. Members do not seek publicity and will only tell their stories if they believe these will be helpful to others experiencing a similar hell.

Margaret is a compulsive gambler on a large scale, and she eventually lost a quarter of a million pounds. It is three years now since she last placed a bet, and her story is typical. She started playing games for money in casinos just after the war. She found casinos very exciting, but for many years managed to keep her compulsion under control. At first, she found it hurt if she lost more than a few pounds.

When her first marriage broke up, she got married again — to a compulsive gambler. He would be out seven nights a week and Margaret was left alone. In the daytime this wasn't a big problem, as Margaret had her own catering business to attend to; but at night she had no company and many hours to fill. She started going to a casino with a married couple and says that as soon as she entered the door she felt different. She became alive and vibrant. Adrenalin rushed through the system as she placed the bets.

Margaret enjoyed casinos because they were smart and welcoming. She soon became a much valued customer, which was not surprising in view of the vast amounts she was losing night after night. The spectacular losers, like Margaret, are treated to free meals and free wines. Before long Margaret began attending casinos on her own, as she found that the company of others interfered with her gambling concentration. She says that when you are gambling heavily you don't need others around you, as life is already almost too exciting.

As with most compulsive gamblers the illness developed gradually. She began to think there was possibly something badly wrong when she couldn't leave the casino until it closed at 4 a.m. Like all gamblers Margaret told herself that whatever she was losing, some day she would win it all back. She wasn't gambling, she was investing. In the end, the situation was so bad that she couldn't bear to spend money on anything but gambling. Even a cup of tea was potential gambling money wasted. The main attraction of gambling, she feels, is that while you are playing all your other troubles simply fade away. You may walk out of your house full of anxieties, but the minute you step inside a casino they vanish. Even though she was getting very little sleep she never felt tired. But she knew her personality was becoming affected. She began to lie, to deceive, and hide what she was doing.

Before very long a £1000 loss in a night meant nothing. By the time she managed to stop gambling, she was dreadfully in debt. Her son suspected something was wrong and, against her wishes, frogmarched his mother to a GA meeting one evening. 'I was afraid I'd have nothing in common with the other gamblers,' Margaret said. 'But I soon realized that you don't need anything else in common. We were all suffering from an identical illness. If it hadn't been for GA I would still be gambling.'

Joseph is another compulsive gambler. Once he started to gamble his business and marriage steadily went downhill, and both broke up. He now feels that gambling is an addiction that has no cure and the most that can be hoped for is that it will be kept under permanent control.

He started to gamble when he was already middle aged and he thought he would be able to keep it within reasonable limits. But before long his business was beginning to show signs of neglect and he would be only half awake in his office. Instead of concentrating on work Joseph would be thinking about the bets he would place in the afternoon.

Money started to become a serious problem, as he could never make enough to feed his compulsion. Life assurance policies were gradually surrendered, and money deposited in building societies for his children also disappeared. It is not at all uncommon for compulsive gamblers to raid their children's money boxes and piggy banks, to go to their wives' purses, or even to steal money out of church collection plates or to forge cheques. All compulsive gamblers stoop to behaviour which they know is despicable, but they can't help it. The compulsion drives them to obtain money from any source or by any means whatever.

Joseph, like Margaret, eventually found his way to Gamblers' Anonymous, where they were both helped to overcome their addictions. This remains the only self-help organization which tries to tackle the gambling problem: but in some ways it does not provide a total answer. Ex-gamblers find that they have to go to GA meetings several times a week, for fear of the addiction coming back if they have an evening alone.

What the Family Can Do

Anybody who suspects that their spouse or partner is in danger of becoming a compulsive gambler, should not just sit back in the hope that the compulsion will go away of its own accord — it won't. Instead, they should find in the phone book the address of the nearest GamAnon branch, and go along for help and advice. Your name will never be revealed and you will be told exactly how to behave, to try and help the afflicted person reverse the gambling habit. Some people give gamblers money, in the mistaken hope that they really will win this time and pay off all their debts. But this never works.

Gamblers have to learn to take responsibility for themselves and cannot be baled out time and again by their partners. This is a mistake that many well-meaning relatives make. The gambler must be kept short of money and not given access to spare cash. Some wives of gamblers arrange for their husbands' salaries to be paid directly into their own accounts, by the firm, so that at least they can have enough money for housekeeping. Many marriages break up through compulsive gambling, because the gambler is unable to behave like an adult. It is often difficult to spot early warning signs, as most gamblers become adept at hiding their behaviour, but at GamAnon families are taught how to interpret the signs. Unaccountable staying out late, unaccountable money disappearances, a perpetually tired look, irritability, anger, guilt, rationalizations, preoccupation, and unnatural interest in the racing results, any adverse personality changes, outright lying — any of these should be suspected.

More men than women become compulsive gamblers, possibly because all gamblers tend to have a highly competitive streak in their behaviour and more men than women like to pit themselves against machines and chance events in the hope that they can beat the odds. It is a trait which has led men to establishing fortunes, but the other side of the coin is the despair and degradation brought about by uncontrolled gambling.

Anybody whose gambling is increasing, or who finds they are spending work time thinking about placing bets, or who continually finds racing results more interesting than other sections of the newspaper, should consider the fact that they may have a gambling problem. Like many diseases it is progressive, and gets worse the more you do it. There is no way that more gambling will help to 'get it out of the system'. This attitude has the opposite effect, driving the habit in even harder. The longer anybody gambles compulsively, the harder the habit is to break.

Anybody who has resorted to rattling their child's piggy bank for gambling money should not delay in going to a GA meeting. New members are always made extremely welcome and the atmosphere is friendly and non-condemnatory. After all, every single person who is there is a compulsive gambler as well. Also, nobody should ever imagine that gambling cannot be controlled. It can, provided there is the wish to stop.

7.

TRANQUILLIZERS

When tranquillizers first appeared on the market about twenty-five years ago they were hailed as the true wonder drug of our time. They were, it seemed, capable of allaying anxiety while enabling people to carry on with their everyday lives as if nothing was wrong. Doctors were told that these pills were not addictive and that they could be prescribed without fear to patients who were suffering from anxiety conditions, phobias, or depression.

At the time, tranquillizers seemed a marvellous answer for doctors who were discovering that they had an increasing number of patients in their surgeries who, while not suffering from any diagnosable illness, were definitely not happy with their lot. So tranquillizers were given to people who had recently experienced a divorce, who were made redundant, who were anxious about giving a speech in public, or who just couldn't seem to cope with everyday life. The wonderful thing was that they seemed to do the trick. Patients who were prescribed them experienced an almost instant lifting of their woes. So after they finished one packet they went back to the doctor for more . . . and more . . . and more. By 1975, about 23 million prescriptions a year were being written out for tranquillizers, making them by far the most prescribed medicine in the country.

Then questions started being asked about tranquillizers and a few people began to worry about them. It was found that many people who had been taking them for years had unaccountably become addicted to them. When they tried to stop taking the pills they experienced a sudden return of all their old anxieties, plus other withdrawal symptoms such as nausea, headaches, shaking legs, and sleeplessness. Although some people probably deliberately misused tranquillizers for their sedating effect, by far the greatest number of addicts were people who had only ever taken them for therapeutic purposes. They became hooked against their will, against their knowledge, and against their intention.

It is estimated that there are about one million long-term tranquillizer users in this country, and that around half of these users will have become physically addicted to the drug.

How Tranquillizers Work

Tranquillizers are actually of two types, known as major and minor. The major ones are used in serious psychiatric illness and are not prescribed to the public at large. It is the so called 'minor' ones that have caused so much trouble with ordinary people. Minor tranquillizers are the group of pills collectively known as benzodiazepines. Individually they go under such names as: diazepam, chlordiazepoxide, medazepam, chloraxepate, lorazepam, temazepam, triazolam, nitrazepam, flurazepam. The commonest brand names are Valium, Librium and Mogadon.

They are classified as psychotropic drugs, which means that they are capable of influencing mood and states of mind. Tranquillizers were invented in the 1950s by Dr Leo Sternbach, who was working for the giant Swiss pharmaceutical company Hoffman-La Roche. At the time, they were considered to be an extremely safe, trouble-free chemical that could have many beneficial effects on mild psychological and psychosomatic disorders. The discovery came about when it was realized that the new laboratory-concocted chemical, later marketed as Valium, could sedate and relax animals, and even tame wild animals. At San Diego Zoo, in 1957, wild cats injected with the new tranquillizing drug became calm and tame. Then it was discovered that with humans the drug could remove most emotional anguish without affecting any other aspect of life. It was soon hailed as a genuine miracle drug which could combat what seemed to be the main disease of the twentieth century — stress.

But over the past ten years evidence has gradually been accumulating that tranquillizers are not such a safe, sure, trouble-free drug as was once supposed. We now know that they can be both physically and psychologically addictive, and can cause severe, long-lasting and quite agonizing withdrawal symptoms in some people.

At first tranquillizers were intended only for short-term use, to help people over a period of extreme stress. But there are around three-quarters of a million people in Britain who have been on tranquillizers for six years or more. In fact, they have become the most widely prescribed repeat drugs in the country, and until recently it was not uncommon for patients simply to ring up for a repeat prescription and then collect it without ever seeing the doctor.

Unlike many other drugs of addiction tranquillizers do not convey any positively pleasurable sensations, but merely allay anxiety for a time. Long-term users often describe a feeling of numbness and drowsiness as a continual state while they are on the drugs.

Basically benzodiazepines decrease the level of consciousness, in rather the same way as alcohol. Although they do not make life's problems go away, they make them seem temporarily insignificant. They depress the central nervous system and damp down all bodily functions. While on tranquillizers, colours, sounds and all sensory impressions are dimmed. In time the chemicals will enter every cell in the body, so that eventually the system comes to rely on them for its daily functioning. In this way, they act in much the same way as heroin or alcohol.

Tranquillizers are fairly fast acting, and a lessening of anxiety will occur within an hour of taking them. Users report that before long they feel floaty and happy. But, as with any addictive drug, the effect wears off within a few hours and another dose of the chemical is needed if anxiety is to be kept down. The pills do not actually remove any troubles but leave them to remain and grow, as many long-term users have discovered to their cost.

Withdrawal Symptoms

People often do not realize just how addictive and pernicious these drugs can be until they try to come off them. As late as 1973 it was said by the medical profession that tranquillizers were not physically addictive, and that they caused no adverse symptoms in the majority of users. In fact it took twenty years for their true addiction potential to be discovered and doctors and patients alike were quite unprepared for the level of dependence that many users had developed.

It is not true to say that every tranquillizer user becomes an addict, and not everybody will experience severe withdrawal symptoms. As with everything else, people vary considerably in their reaction to tranquillizers. But the main problem is that people can become dependent without ever realizing it. Most people know whether they are addicted to alcohol, heroin or cigarettes, but they may have no idea how dependent they have become on tranquillizers. It is only when they try to withdraw that the true extent of the addiction is realized. It has been said that coming off tranquillizers can actually be far worse than trying to withdraw from heroin. Alcohol-abuse charities say that when their patients are prescribed Valium to help them cope with withdrawal from alcohol, they can then find it extremely difficult to come off the tranquillizers.

With tranquillizers the dependence is physical rather than psychological. A study undertaken at the Wolfson Unit of Clinical Pharmacology at the Royal Victoria Infirmary, Newcastle, discovered that a quarter of patients who had been taking benzodiazepines for four months had already become dependent on them. Other users will show definite withdrawal symptoms after just a few weeks.

Professor Malcolm Lader of the Institute of Psychiatry, who has been studying the effects of tranquillizers for many years, told a meeting of the Royal Society that there were major withdrawal symptoms in a significant number of patients. At first it had been thought that tolerance and dependence developed only at very high doses, but now doctors are realizing that normal doses can cause serious addiction problems as well. One study showed that forty-five per cent of long-term users — average time thirteen years — had typical withdrawal symptoms after being taken off the drug. Not only that but they experienced a renewal of all their old anxiety problems. Professor Lader likened withdrawal symptoms in many patients to a mild form of *delerium tremens*, and added that people often became extremely depressed when the drug was removed from their life. He said that this depression is not always a return of the old trouble but can appear as a completely new difficulty.

The commonest withdrawal symptoms are perceptual disturbances, which include an increased sensitivity to all forms of sensory stimulation — light, colour, food, heat and cold. There may also be an impression of continuous movement, and a feeling that you don't know who you are or where you are. These feelings of disorientation can be extremely traumatic and may last for several weeks, or even months, depending on how long the drug has been taken.

Withdrawal can also be accompanied by physical changes such as weight loss and changes in heartbeat and blood-pressure. In some people epileptic seizures can occur and behaviour may border on the psychotic or paranoid. There may be hallucinations and also sleeplessness, fear, agitation, lack of concentration, palpitations, a choking feeling, dry mouth, hot and cold sensations, trembling hands, loss of appetite, nausea, weakness in the legs, irritability and disturbed sleep. Not everybody will suffer all these effects, but as with any drug withdrawal it cannot be known in advance who will experience bad symptoms.

The withdrawal syndrome appears within two to three days of stopping the pills and the worst effects usually last for about two weeks. In some people, however, these symptoms can persist for many months. The symptoms may be so severe that the doctor may advise re-starting the drug and trying again to withdraw from it more slowly. As there are many different tranquillizers now on the market it is as well to know in advance which ones cause particular symptoms. Some of the benzodiazepines are short acting, others long acting, and the withdrawal symptoms will be different in each case. Those leading to bad withdrawal symptoms in a significant number of people are: oxazepam, triazolam, temazepam and lorazepam. It seems that lorazepam and temazepam are particularly difficult to withdraw from. To find out how to withdraw successfully, you should first ask your doctor which drug you were on in the first place.

There have been so many stories now of tranquillizer addiction and horrific withdrawal that many patients are afraid to stop taking them suddenly and, in fact, this is not recommended. The 'cold turkey' approach is not the best course of action for tranquillizer takers.

Professor Lader, who has been outspoken about tranquillizers for many years and has issued several warnings against their long-term use, feels that they have truly become the 'opium of the people', far more than actual opium or its derivatives, such as heroin or methadone.

In her book *The Tranquilliser Trap*, which analyses the current situation as regards tranquillizers, Joy Melville says that most patients are quite unprepared for the severity of the reaction when they decide to withdraw after several years' continuous use. Fear and terror can set in because, apart from any physical symptoms that may be noticed, there is the realization that they have now lost an intimate friend, an ever-ready and willing helper, and a solution to life's difficulties.

Facing up to life again without tranquillizers can be a very nerve-racking step to take. Those who have achieved it are in no doubt that it is entirely worth it, although often painful in the extreme.

Anybody who has read Barbara Gordon's book, *I'm Dancing as Fast as I Can*, will know how horrifying the results of tranquillizer addiction can be.

Case History

Anita Gordon was on Valium for fifteen years. It was not until she tried to manage without tranquillizers that she realized she had become an addict and that her system had come to depend on the pills. A few years ago she started her own organization, *Tranx Release*, to help others in the same position as herself. There are now about seventy self-help organizations scattered around the country to encourage people to come off tranquillizers.

Anita's story started when her first marriage was breaking up. She was prescribed tranquillizers and the doctor told her she could expect to be on Valium for the rest of her life. At the time, she says, she didn't even question this, but accepted it quite happily. She felt that the doctors knew best and put her faith in them. She was advised to take three tablets a day and, at first, thought they really were a miracle drug.

'Only a few days after taking the first lot,' Anita said, 'my troubles and anxieties really did lift and go away. I felt so much clearer and better and instantly I could cope with life.' Only a few months after being on the drugs, however, she would have days where she screamed and shouted for no apparent reason. She never connected this irrational behaviour with the drugs she was taking, however, and after receiving her initial prescription, she never saw the doctor again. Whenever she needed more pills she would just ring up the receptionist, who would write out a repeat dose.

After she had been on the drugs for several years, Anita remarried and changed doctors. When her new doctor saw that she was on Valium he automatically continued the prescription without ever asking Anita why she was taking these tablets; nor did she think to discuss the situation with her new doctor. Anita then became pregnant and he took her off the pills. 'I felt absolutely dreadful,' Anita remembers, 'and so he put me straight back on them.'

Anita continued to take the pills all through her pregnancy, and a subsequent one, and blessed them. She took it for granted that she needed them and her system became acclimatized to them. After moving to Northampton, where she now lives, the prescriptions went on as before. Her new husband did advise her to try and come off the pills, but she wouldn't listen to him.

She still felt sure that the doctor knew best.

Then a new doctor, who was anti-drug, joined the practice and asked to see Mrs Gordon. 'He wanted to know why I was on the drugs, and after a long talk, he said I didn't need them. He did say that it would now be dangerous to try and come off them just like that, and gave me a month's supply of a different drug, Ativan.

'The idea was that the new drug would help my system get used to not having daily doses of Valium. But they were horrible drugs. After taking them for a few days, I thought I was going mad. I started to have dreadful panic attacks, and didn't know what was happening. I also had bad stomach cramps, nausea and sleeplessness. None of these symptoms had been present while I was on Valium. In fact I felt fine for most of the time.

'I threw these drugs away, and decided to try and live without any pills at all. That was very definitely the very worst period of my whole life. I became very frightened. I was afraid to stand in front of the washing machine, even, and I wouldn't get into the car. In the winter, it snowed, and I was frightened of that — it was so white and brilliant. I realized then that, while on Valium, all colours and impressions were dimmed. I also became very sensitive to light, and had to sit watching the television wearing sunglasses. Tranquillizers, I came to learn, blunt the whole of your perception.'

If these had been the only effects Anita reckons it wouldn't have been too bad. But far worse than any of this was the return of the old anxiety. One day, about seven months after she had come off the pills, she just sat in the garden and cried and cried. All she could think about was her first marriage, which had ended fifteen years previously. She understood then that Valium doesn't remove anxiety, but just buries it deep in the system. After fifteen years all the hurt and upset caused by her first marriage was still there. Anita says:

> The drugs ensure that the anxiety remains, so that it all surges back up again when you stop taking them. I was going through very severe withdrawal symptoms. Part of the problem was that, while on the drugs I did feel confident and able to cope, yet I was only half alive.
>
> When I go out into the garden now I am aware of things growing. But I simply didn't notice them before. I feel now that those fifteen years were wasted, spent as a zombie and not really living at all.
>
> Looking back, I now know that I could have coped by myself, but I never gave myself a chance. I took what seemed at the time

an easy way out, but I have certainly paid for it since. I know now that you can't suppress anger and hurt, but have to let them get out of the system completely. When you take tranquillizers, everything seems to stay inside, even physical pain. Some of the members of Tranx Release say that when they stop taking Valium all their physical aches and pains come back. Your system is damped down, but nothing is actually ever cured.

Through the widespread use of tranquillizers I feel we have now got ourselves a new social problem, a new disease. My advice to everybody now is: if you are going through physical or emotional disturbances in your life, be very careful indeed before you accept any long-term medication. I don't actually think that emotional difficulties, such as I was going through, can be treated medically. Personal help and advice is the answer.

Anita Gordon's salvation lay in contacting a self-help group for women just like herself. 'I spoke to a lady in Essex who had experienced exactly the same problems as myself. She told me there would be a lot of mental and physical symptoms, but that they would pass. She also advised me that it was important to mourn the death of my first marriage properly, and get it right out of the system. It took about ten months before I realized I was getting more good days than bad.' Anita also went to see a hypnotist, and found this helped a lot.

The Position Now
As the physical and psychological effects of tranquillizers become ever more apparent, people are increasingly wondering whether these drugs should be taken at all. From being considered the wonder drug of the century tranquillizers are now so feared that many people simply will not consider them. Doctors were very slow throughout the 1970s to realize just how addictive these drugs could be, but now the evidence has become irrefutable and their patients have mostly heard stories of the unpleasant effects that tranquillizers can produce.

Any psychoactive drug should be approached with extreme caution, whether this is alcohol, nicotine or a drug prescribed by the doctor; but this does not mean such drugs have no useful part to play. In certain complaints, and with certain kinds of treatment, tranquillizers can be extremely efficacious. Dr Peter Nixon, consultant cardiologist at Charing Cross Hospital, believes in Valium, but only for very short periods and for absolutely specific purposes.

Dr Nixon often gives Valium to patients suffering from severe heart conditions, to calm and sedate them, and enable them to recover to some extent from the exhaustion that has brought about the heart attack. Valium is not seen as a cure, but it enables people to rest and relax and gives them 'time out' from their ordinary cares and worries. This can mean that the body has a chance to begin the work of physical recovery, as demands are temporarily lifted. But tranquillizers are only used by Dr Nixon for a couple of weeks and only under the strictest hospital supervision, after the person has been admitted as an in-patient. Patients are not given repeat prescriptions when they leave hospital. Valium can also be useful for people undergoing dental treatment and in certain kinds of surgery. It is a muscle relaxant and can definitely help people over a specific medical crisis.

But before taking a mood-altering drug for any other purpose, important questions should be asked. Anybody suffering from a recent bereavement, a terrible shock, or sudden grief, can undoubtedly gain relief from a course of tranquillizers. They do not lessen the pain but alter perception of it, so that the worst effects are simply not felt. But it must be remembered that, as with any chemical solution to emotional pain, the drug does not make the problem disappear. Like heroin or alcohol, tranquillizers can make the problem seem temporarily insignificant, but it will have to be coped with at some stage. There is a school of thought which says it is better to grieve at the time, and get this out of the system, rather than keeping it inside by use of tranquillizers.

During the 1960s and '70s there was a tendency to go to the doctor for any kind of trouble that had an emotional or mental component, such as a phobia, depression or anxiety. The idea then was that there would be a pill available for every ill, and that there were easy solutions to such problems in life. Now we know that tranquillizers can extract a very high price for the blanking-out effect that they deliver. There is no evidence that long-term use of tranquillizers can actually wreck bodily functions, in the way that alcohol and heroin can, the problem is that the emotional trauma will have to be faced when the drug is discontinued, and that the physical withdrawal symptoms, in the short term, may be unexpectedly severe. Normal functioning will eventually return, but in the meantime the original trouble, the reason for taking the pills in the first place, will have to be faced.

It seems now that nobody should consider taking tranquillizers for more than a few weeks. A paper in the *British Medical Journal* suggested that their calming effect only lasts for a couple of weeks anyway and that after this length of time they are no more use than a dummy pill, or placebo. The paper went on to say that the pills were not even very effective and for people suffering from anxiety no better than sympathetic advice or counselling. The drugs are most often given for anxiety and insomnia, both problems that are not easily resolved by any means.

Those who are suffering chronically from either of these problems should definitely seek a non-drug solution to their problem. Sleeping pills do put people out for the night, but they do not enable natural, beneficial sleep to take place. They have more of a knock-out, anaesthetizing effect. Rather than risk becoming addicted to a mood-altering chemical, individuals should seek other, more permanent and satisfactory ways of becoming relaxed and able to sleep. Dr Malcolm Carruthers, of the Maudsley Hospital, has said that 'meditation not medication should be the prescription of the Eighties'. Any exercises which relax the body without being competitive or tiring, such as yoga, or meditation classes, can be far more effective than a pill from the doctor in combating anxiety problems and there are no harmful side-effects. Doing yoga or meditating may be less easy than swallowing a pill, and may require more work in the first instance, but it is worth it.

Those who are suffering from an actual psychiatric disorder or severe mental disturbance may need drug treatment, but that does not account for the majority of people who are prescribed tranquillizers. By far the greatest number of users are ordinary people who feel depressed, or who have the impression that life is too much to bear, and feel that everything is getting on top of them.

Professor Lader has measured the shape and size of the brains of twenty patients who had been taking Valium for five to ten years, three times a day, and found that only five still had normal-sized brains. Tranquillizers decrease the level of consciousness, which in turn affects all perception. It seems that those who have been taking tranquillizers for any length of time actually risk becoming less intelligent, as happens with any addictive drug.

Tranquillizers are prescribed mainly to women and it is estimated that over a quarter of all women aged forty-five or more will have been prescribed them at some stage in their life, usually to cope with 'women's troubles'. The message is coming home ever clearer now that there is no pill, no seductive substance, that can ever help people to overcome life's problems. All the chemical can do is to mask them for a time, whilst wreaking havoc with mental processes and, in many cases, bodily systems as well.

Coming Off Tranquillizers

At first it was assumed that as these pills seemed to be so innocuous, and did not cause any terrible side-effects while people were taking them, that stopping them would be a simple matter. But the story of Anita Gordon and those of countless others have shown that this is not so. Coming off tranquillizers is a very serious matter and cannot be undertaken lightly.

Nobody should ever fear that, because the withdrawal symptoms may be uncomfortable and distressing, perhaps they are better off staying on the pills. That is never an answer. Although withdrawal symptoms may be bad, they will pass and the anxieties connected with their use will pass as well. But it can be difficult, and indeed dangerous, to try and come off the pills entirely alone. First of all, tell your doctor that you intend to come off the tranquillizers and see what the reaction is. A sensible doctor will advise cutting down the dosage gradually, so the body gets used to a smaller dose. This enables it to cope better.

Even if your doctor does seem sensible, and has all the right ideas about stopping tranquillizers, any user would be well advised to get in touch with a tranquillizer withdrawal group. Release, the drug-advice agency, produce a very useful leaflet advising people how to come off tranquillizers, which gives an indication of what they might expect.

Joan Jerome started one of the earliest Tranx Release groups, and she describes how it works. This pattern has been emulated by other tranquillizer groups up and down the country. She says:

Our organization grew from a small group which met in December 1982 in my house. In December 1983 the DHSS awarded us a grant, so we moved in April to our own building in Harrow. We now have a full time, paid co-ordinator, and a full time secretary, plus several volunteer workers.

Tranx now deals with an average of 200 new referrals a month, and gets 35 to 45 calls for help a day. Most of the clients are middle aged and three-quarters of them are women. We now have 1,500 people on our books, mainly from the Brent and Harrow area.

Most of our clients come of their own accord, but more and more are being referred to us by doctors, psychiatrists, social workers and so on.

We believe that people come of their own accord either because the GP does not understand the problem or has no time to deal with it. Most of the people who join our organization tell us that their doctor said the symptoms were all in their mind, or that they would disappear in anything from 72 hours to three weeks.

But we now know that the average recovery time is six weeks for every year the pills have been taken. During this time withdrawals reach several peaks, with good periods in between. It is when there is a relapse after a good period that most people fall back into the pill cycle because, at this point, the doctor will say, 'I told you, you needed those pills.'

Joan Jerome believes that recovery takes a very long time, physically and psychologically, and that a lot of support is needed from doctors, family and friends. She is worried that doctors, in their desperation to help patients who are suffering agonies when trying to withdraw from tranquillizers, will prescribe far more powerful drugs, such as Melleril and Largactil, the so-called 'major' tranquillizers, used for psychiatric cases. All of these, she says, set patients back in their recovery.

Joan Jerome's considered view is that it is virtually impossible to recover from tranquillizer addiction without the support of a self-help group and being able to talk to people who have been through the ordeal themselves. Although she believes that tranquillizers can lead to serious addiction problems, and does not condone their use, she urges doctors not to take their patients off the drugs all at once, and not to prescribe anything for the withdrawal symptoms. This could mean that the patients become hooked on the new pills. She is of the firm opinion that nature does its work by itself and that people can recover, given the right kind of non-drug help and support. Recovery is perfectly possible, although people must be prepared for it to take some time. As a generalization, the longer a person has been on tranquillizers the longer she will take to recover from their adverse effects. Tolerance builds up in the system, as with any strong drug. Joan Jerome says that most of the people who have attended her group have made their own decision to come off the drugs, and mostly they are eventually successful.

No one should imagine that the addiction cannot be broken or that the present pain means that it is not worth persevering. Everybody who has been on tranquillizers for a long time but is now free is in no doubt as to which is better, life on the pills or off them. People actually become stronger and more successful when they are able to deal with life's crises without resorting to the pill or the bottle.

Professor Lader has said that we have become, as a nation, more and more intolerant of any kind of pain or distress, whether this is mental or physical, feeling that there must be a treatment for all ills. But we are now coming to realize, increasingly, that for the most part all healing is self-healing. A period of grief may be needed to break attachment with somebody who is now dead or who has gone away permanently. Depression, anxiety, phobias, sleeplessness, are all there for a reason. Tranquillizers never enable people to discover what that reason is, so they can never overcome it.

8.

NICOTINE

Introduction

In spite of all the anti-smoking propaganda that has been issued over the past few years people continue to smoke. There can be few adults in Britain or elsewhere who have not tried smoking at some point. Some will never acquire the taste but a substantial proportion will eventually become hooked. Although there are fewer smokers around than used to be the case, almost one-third of all adults in Britain still smoke.

Many adult men have given up over the past few years, but the numbers of women and young people who smoke remains high. Nicotine, the main active ingredient in cigarettes, definitely causes dependence but unlike other addictive substances it does not alter perception or change the personality in significant ways. Smokers do not become deviant deceitful zombies in the same way that addicts of other substances can. This has led some scientists to remark that nicotine is not a real addiction at all and that it can be given up quite easily, once a decision has been reached to stop smoking.

Nowadays many people who smoke do not want to do so. At one time cigarettes undoubtedly had a highly sophisticated image. Royalty, including George VI and the Duke of Windsor, statesmen like Winston Churchill, and nearly all leading film stars of the 1940s and '50s smoked publicly. Now the only people who smoke in films and television plays are the obvious bad guys. Smoking is now prohibited in many cinemas, it is not advertised on television, and more restaurants and public places are being designated no-smoking areas. Anybody who smokes nowadays almost risks being considered a social outcast.

The health risks connected with cigarettes have been well documented, not just for those who smoke but also for those who live with smokers. In fact, 'passive smoking' is considered by some to be almost as great a health risk as active smoking. Unborn babies can be adversely affected by smoking parents, and several studies have indicated that wives of heavy-smoking men risk heart attacks and earlier death than wives of non-smokers.

How easy is it to become addicted to smoking, and what are the pains and problems associated with giving up?

The Nature of Nicotine Addiction

It appears that the smoking habit, as with other forms of drug addiction, is closely related to personality. Hans Eysenck, formerly Professor of Psychiatry at the Institute of Psychiatry, has investigated some of the reasons why people smoke and why others, with equal access to cigarettes, are never attracted to the habit. His conclusion is that smokers tend to be more restless, extrovert and stimulation-seeking than non-smokers. Also, they are liable to drink more and to divorce more often.

Studies of smokers' brains have shown that such people very often have a good deal of high frequency activity going on inside their heads. This can mean they find it difficult to relax and calm down. Eysenck postulates that most smokers would find it extremely hard to meditate. Non-smokers, by contrast, tend to find life sufficiently exciting without the introduction of an artificial stimulus such as nicotine.

But is smoking a genuine addiction? Most smokers, especially those who have tried and failed to give up, would undoubtedly say yes. But a study of 2,700 smokers carried out by the Office of Population, Census and Surveys argues that smoking is more of a 'learned dependence' than a true addiction. The study said that most people find it extremely easy to give up, once they have decided that they do not want to be smokers any more.

The study went on to say that over the past ten years one in five former smokers has managed to give up. According to Alan Marsh, the social psychiatrist who carried out the survey, the power of nicotine to produce dependence cannot have mysteriously lessened over the years just because the health risks became more apparent. He concluded that the power of nicotine to produce addiction had been over-emphasized and, a non-smoker himself, stated that all tobacco users were 'overgrown teenagers' who hadn't yet reached adulthood. As soon as they did, he declared, they would be able to give up their habit quite easily.

But there is no doubt that nicotine interacts in a complex way with the body and the brain. Nicotine dependence is by no means 'all in the mind' and the addiction is probably physical rather than psychological, although the ritual aspect of tobacco smoking — the actual lighting up — has to be taken into account, as with all other addictions. When the cigarette smoker inhales, about twenty-five per cent of the nicotine contained in the smoke reaches the brain twice as quickly as an injection of heroin, although the results are less dramatically felt. A twenty-a-day smoker would receive between 50,000 and 70,000 such shots of nicotine a year. Nicotine also causes the heart to beat faster, makes the blood vessels constrict and blood-pressure rise.

At first nicotine has the effect of sharpening thinking and brain power. In fact, some studies on smokers have indicated that they become more alert seconds after taking their first drag: they wake up and seem more alive.

But, as with any other drug, nicotine buoys you up only to let you down not much later. After a few hours, heart-rate has slowed right down, blood-pressure has dropped, and the mind has lost its alert edge. All the classic withdrawal symptoms are experienced and there is an overwhelming desire to have another cigarette.

As a drug, nicotine is capable of producing highly contradictory effects on the body. When it first hits the brain it galvanizes nerve connections into action, but later it blocks them. It stimulates the flow of adrenalin for a time, but then shuts it down. Nicotine wakes up the nerves in muscles, then causes a kind of paralysis. It also has the effect of reducing hunger by stopping gastric contractions and it can increase metabolic rate. This is why new ex-smokers often put on weight after stopping. Hunger increases, although, like most withdrawal symptoms, this effect is felt only for a short time.

Dr Michael Russell, of the Maudsley Hospital, London, who has closely studied the effects of smoking, disagrees with Alan Marsh on the matter of nicotine addiction. He said, 'Cigarette smoking is probably the most addictive and dependence forming behaviour known to humans.'

In its effect, nicotine lies somewhere between the mood-changing drugs and alcohol abuse. It is not yet clear exactly how tobacco affects the brain, but we do know that it can be both stimulating and sedative at the same time. Withdrawal symptoms can include decreased heart-rate, restlessness, loss of sleep, headaches, amnesia and impairment of judgement.

It seems clear that people continue to smoke to gain the effect of a pharmacologically active drug and that deprivation soon results in a craving for more. Around ninety per cent of smokers simply cannot bear the pain of withdrawal, and this drives them to seek another cigarette. In time, it becomes just like any other addiction: it's not so much the pleasure of the cigarettes themselves, but the fear of withdrawal symptoms that keeps most smokers puffing away. Also, as with any other form of addiction, the ritual surrounding cigarette smoking is an important aspect of the habit. Buying cigarettes, taking off the cellophane wrapping, taking off the gold paper and extracting a new, aromatic cigarette from the pack are almost as important as the pharmacological aspects of smoking. They are, for the smoker, what preparing the fix is for the heroin addict. All addictions, including that of cigarette smoking, are extremely time-consuming and not least of the smoker's problems is what to do with all those minutes in the day that previously would have been filled up by cigarettes.

Who Smokes and Why?

Over ninety-five per cent of smokers take up the habit as teenagers. It is extremely rare for anybody to begin smoking in their late twenties: if a teenager does not start smoking at school or college then it is very unlikely that he or she will become a smoker in later life. Also, many people who smoke as teenagers find that they no longer need the habit once these stress-filled years are over.

Even nowadays, with all the anti-smoking propaganda (or perhaps even *because* of it), over a quarter of all teenagers over the age of sixteen are regular smokers. It is now common practice in local authority children's homes to allow smoking from the age of fourteen, as social workers have found it absolutely impossible to outlaw it after that age. Nowhere in the adult world is smoking now encouraged, as it once was, so why is the habit still so common among young people?

A new study, undertaken in the North of England of over 15,000 children between the ages of eight and nineteen, provides some of the answers. In this survey, published in the *Journal of the Royal College of General Practitioners* in October 1984, children from sixty-five state and independent schools in Cumbria and in Tyne and Wear, were questioned about their smoking beliefs and habits. Although most of the children questioned were fully aware of the health risks, other considerations over-rode these and persuaded them to smoke.

Thirty-nine per cent of girls aged fourteen to sixteen smoked to show off, ten per cent because they felt it looked tough, and another twenty-six per cent because they said it appeared grown up. But the overwhelming reason given for smoking, in this age group, was that it calmed the nerves. Forty-five per cent of girls felt it helped them to keep their weight down and thirty-eight per cent said it imparted confidence. Of the boys in the same age group, thirty-five per cent said they smoked to show off and seventy-two per cent because it calmed their nerves. Thirty-one per cent of the boys also said it gave them added confidence.

At a meeting of the British Association for the Advancement of Science, delegates in Cambridge heard that a study of 4,400 pupils in Sheffield schools showed that girls were now more likely than boys to start smoking. Further, a World Health Organization report on teenage smoking said that, all over the world, it was girls rather than boys who were tending to take up the habit. In several countries now there are more teenage girls smoking than boys — something quite new in smoking trends.

David Simpson, the Director of ASH — Action on Smoking and Health — thinks that teenage girls are now being exploited as a new growth area for cigarette advertising. He feels that the level of cigarette advertising in magazines aimed at young women is unacceptably high. Yet, as we know, although advertising may encourage a compulsion it can't create it. Girls are not smoking more *simply* because more cigarettes are aimed at them, though this may be a factor.

The Health Education Council has now launched a 'Pacesetters' campaign aimed at persuading young people not to smoke. The Parliamentary Secretary for Health said: 'Many youngsters undoubtedly start because they see it as a sophisticated or grown-up thing to do.'

Over the past few years special attention has also been paid to women smokers, who are giving up the habit far less readily than men. Cigarette smoking was an early sign of female emancipation, and women first began smoking in large numbers during the Second World War. Women find the habit harder to kick partly because, until recently, all health studies were carried out on male smokers and women did not identify with these. But secondly, and more importantly, it is believed that many women continue to smoke because it makes them seem more grown up and sophisticated — exactly the same reasons why teenagers take up the habit.

In her book *The Ladykillers: Why Smoking is a Feminist Issue*, Bobbie Jacobson said that women smoke as a way of having time to themselves, to do their own thing. When women are surrounded by small children all day, smoking is one activity that distances and distinguishes them from the toddlers underfoot. Having a cigarette can become a woman's only way of having some time to herself in a day filled with the demands of others. For some women also, smoking may be seen as a symbol both of power and indulgence. It is something you do for yourself.

The health dangers connected with women and smoking have been aimed not so much at the women themselves, as at the possible effects on unborn babies and the increased risk of still birth. For many years now pregnant women have been encouraged not to smoke, but as Doreen Taylor pointed out in an article in *The Guardian* this is still viewing women not so much as people in their own right, as adjuncts to someone else. Women are giving up smoking at a slower rate than men and are, largely, ignoring the warnings about lung cancer, heart disease and other ills. Reports that women who are over thirty-five, and who smoke, and take the contraceptive pill risk a higher incidence of thrombosis, has had the effect of making women change their contraceptive, rather than give up smoking.

A big fear among women smokers is that, if they do give up, they will immediately put on unwanted weight. In fact, this happens only if the former addiction results in another one being taken up. If you simply substitute food for cigarettes, then of course extra weight will be the result.

The Health Risks

When a smoker inhales he takes in with the smoke at least 4,000 different chemicals, which include carbon monoxide, nitrogen dioxide gases, and toxic hydrogen cyanide. All of these are carcinogens, i.e. cancer-causing agents. Most chemical vapours contained in tobacco are deposited in the mouth, nose, throat and lungs in the form of tar. It is in this tar that most of the cancer-causing chemicals remain.

Cigarette smoking is undoubtedly not good for physical health, but the extent to which it does harm is somewhat under dispute. There are nearly ten million smokers in Britain, according to ASH, and almost 100,000 premature deaths a year are smoking-related. It is what the Royal College of Physicians has termed 'the hidden holocaust'. One of their estimates is that out of one thousand young men who smoke, statistically speaking, one will be murdered, six will die in road accidents, and two hundred and fifty will die prematurely as a result of smoking.

About a quarter of deaths from coronary heart disease appear to be related to tobacco, and ASH says that at least 19,000 preventable deaths occur each year from tobacco smoking. But this has not been proved beyond all doubt. Some doctors are saying that cigarette smoking does not increase the risk of heart disease, while others aver that not even lung cancer may be as directly connected with smoking as we have imagined. Hans Eysenck said: 'Only one in ten heavy smokers develops lung cancer: why don't the other nine? The link between personality and smoking should not be ignored.'

The nicotine effect is probably similar to that of other drugs. Although smoke entering the body is definitely harmful, some systems will be strong enough to combat it while other people may succumb to the ill effects very quickly. Also there is always the danger that, when anybody gives up an addictive habit such as smoking, they will merely substitute another drug for the one now dropped. It is true that, over the past thirty years, the number of doctors who smoke has halved; but Kenneth Rawnsley, President of the Royal College of Psychiatrists, believes that many have taken to drink instead. He told a meeting of the Medical Council on Alcoholism that doctors are now three times more likely than the rest of the population to die of alcoholism, and to develop cirrhosis of the liver.

Between 1931 and 1971 the numbers of doctors dying from lung cancer halved, but the figures might not be as encouraging as might at first appear. Research statistician Peter Lee, in a study reported in *The Lancet*, found that, although doctors who reduced their smoking suffered less from smoking-related diseases, they were succumbing instead to other forms of stress. His study showed that between 1951 and 1971 doctors reduced their smoking far more than other men in similar social classes, but that they were now turning to drink instead.

As nicotine is known to exert both a calming and a stimulating influence, we must also consider the good side of cigarettes. Smoking definitely does reduce stress, not only in the mind but in physical ways as well; and if giving up smoking makes a person more stressed, then they may even be better off continuing with the habit.

Giving Up

However, most, if not all smokers will tell you that they wish they could give up. How easy is it, in fact?

This all depends on a person's motivation. It is easy to give up smoking if the smoker has made a conscious decision that he or she does not want to be a smoker any more. Where there is a powerful wish to give up, then it will be possible to break the dependency. But many smokers do not, in their heart of hearts, want to give up, and that is why they continue to smoke. They perceive that they get more out of continuing to smoke than they would if they gave up, and so they carry on.

Many people who try to give up find themselves becoming irritable, moody and unable to concentrate; and they too turn back to cigarettes after a time. It is not unknown for people to start suddenly at a time of crisis, maybe many years after relinquishing the habit. It has been estimated that it takes about eleven years to remove a long-established tobacco addiction from every cell in the body, and at any time up to then the habit could take hold again.

Those who are serious about giving up smoking can do it quite easily on their own. Unlike certain other addictions, giving up smoking is not something that requires outside help — although this may give extra motivation to some people. As tobacco smoking does not affect physical functioning in the same way as tranquillizers, heroin or alcohol, the withdrawal symptoms will not be so agonizing to the body.

A Personal Story: I was a dedicated smoker for over twenty years and, although perfectly aware of the health risks, imagined I could never give up. I felt that cigarettes were as essential to me as life itself and could not understand how other people could get through the day without one. But, five years ago, I decided I no longer wanted to be a smoker. Having made that decision, I systematically set about stopping the habit. I chose to cut down gradually, rather than instant withdrawal although others will say there is no substitute for stopping altogether, immediately. It depends to a large extent on choosing the method that suits you best. I would choose times for having a cigarette. At first, I decided to have ten a day and pre-picked the time for these.

After a short time, I felt I could cut down to five a day, and allotted times to smoke these. Gradually, this became three a day, then two, then one, until the day when I had none at all. This was an agonizing day, I remember, and I tried to kill the craving with sugarless chewing gum. As the days went on, and I substituted chewing gum for cigarettes, my jaws began to ache with the constant chewing. I then had to give up chewing the gum.

The next step was to avoid, where possible, all places I had previously associated with cigarettes, such as pubs and restaurants. The most difficult thing of all, I found, was not having a cigarette along with an alcoholic drink. Previously, I had associated one with the other. I enrolled at an exercise class in the lunch hour, to try and overcome the terrible cravings I felt for cigarettes at this time.

I would say that it took two weeks for the very worst of the craving to die down, during which time I was bad tempered, lacking in concentration, and once or twice had too much to drink. But this acute craving gradually gave way to a dull ache which, after a few months, subsided altogether. Part of the problem is giving up the ritual aspect, and also deciding what to do with those odd pockets of time during the day when you would previously have smoked. The exercise was made doubly difficult for me, as in my job as a journalist I would automatically light up when making a phone call, or when rolling a sheet of paper into the typewriter. But in the end all the cravings and symptoms passed and now I am firmly of the anti-smoking brigade. These days I hate the smell of cigarette smoke, hate being near people who smoke, and find it difficult to understand how anybody can persist with such a foul habit.

It is not possible to give up an addiction unless you are able to replace it with something more positive. As we have said before nature hates a vacuum, and anybody embarking on the difficult matter of giving up smoking must ask themselves why they want to give up and what they will do instead with all that spare time. In my case the solution was to work harder so that, in the end, it actually became an annoying interruption to stop work and light up a cigarette. Other people discover that an absorbing hobby, jogging, or yoga and meditation can help to kill the craving.

Martin Raw, of the Department of Psychology, St George's Hospital Medical School, London says that if smokers are not strongly motivated to stop then no treatment will work, whereas if they are then almost any treatment will work.

Treatment clinics

There are around fifty of these in England and Wales, and they are mostly operated by area health education departments. They mainly offer group discussion, mutual support and health information. Success rates are not spectacularly high, about ten to twenty per cent in the long term. Some centres have tried drug therapy, such as tranquillizers, to relieve withdrawal symptoms, but this method has not proved effective.

Hypnosis

This is offered mainly by private hypnotherapists and there can be a good rate of success, so long as the smoker truly wants to stop. A good hypnotist will first discover whether the subject actually does want to give up and will be honest about the results. Hypnotherapists all say that there is nothing they can do to help the person who subconsciously wants to carry on smoking. Hypnosis does not in itself impart willpower and it is not true that your mind can be 'taken over' under hypnosis: it is only your own deep wishes that can be brought out. Anybody considering this form of treatment should make sure they go to a reputable practitioner. The Society of Medical and Dental Hypnosis has a list of hypnotherapists who will help with smoking problems.

Nicotine chewing gum

This was developed by a Swedish company, A.B. Leo, of Helsingborg, and is sold under the brand name of Nicorette. It is available on prescription, and many doctors think it works very well. Most smokers dislike the gum at first and they must be carefully trained in its use. It should not be handed out like any other prescription but accompanied by counselling and the promise of support and follow-up. Again, the smoker must be genuinely motivated to stop otherwise the chewing gum cannot work. It is not magic.

The gum is available in two strengths, each piece containing either 2 mg or 4 mg of nicotine. About ninety per cent of the nicotine is released within half an hour of chewing. A 4 mg piece of gum chewed every hour for two to three hours produces nicotine concentrations in the blood which are similar to those found in heavy cigarette smokers. The effect on heart-rate and blood-pressure is similar to cigarette smoking.

The gum works by providing nicotine to overcome withdrawal symptoms and to substitute for the oral satisfaction gained in cigarette smoking. The idea is that smokers will be enabled to break the habit in two stages: first of all, the link with actually smoking cigarettes is broken; and secondly, the nicotine dependence is gradually lessened. It seems, from clinical trials conducted so far, that the gum really does encourage people to give up. It has a nasty taste, and there are some side-effects which may be experienced by a minority of users. Some people have reported that the gum causes irritation of the tongue, mouth and throat, and others say they feel sick during the first week of not smoking. These effects occur partly because smokers chew the gum too vigorously, in an attempt to gain the nicotine effect quickly.

It is important to realize that the gum is not a straight substitute for cigarettes. It does not reproduce all the effects of smoking because the nicotine is absorbed far more slowly. The gum must be chewed slowly otherwise irritation may set in. People can take several days to learn to chew it properly, but the trick is to learn to chew to release and absorb the nicotine at a rate that is right for each individual. For a time, most smokers will continue to use cigarettes as well. Very few people, it has been found, are able to stop smoking at once, even with Nicorette.

Herbal cigarettes

These can also be useful for some people. Cigarettes containing coltsfoot are supposed to give some of the satisfactions associated with smoking, but as they do not contain nicotine they help to lessen dependence on this substance.

Herbal cigarettes are less addictive than the other kind, but at the same time it must be said that they do not deliver anything like the same level of satisfaction. Many people who try them give up only to return to proper smoking not long after. The drawback with herbal cigarettes is that, like sugar substitutes, they keep the actual habit alive.

What Parents Can Do

As with all other bad habits, the best way of stopping children from smoking is to set a good example. Children are less likely to smoke if they have been brought up in a non-smoking home. But it must be remembered that by far the great majority of children will try cigarettes at some stage. Here, the wise parent does not over-condemn, as this could have the effect of making the child even more attracted to the habit, out of a spirit of rebellion. Obviously, no parent can actually ever stop a child from smoking.

It is probably best not to dwell too heavily on the health dangers of smoking, as every child will know of someone who has smoked fifty cigarettes a day for many years without any apparent ill effects. Also, very few young people are over-concerned about their health: that worry sets in later, usually when some indications of ill health have manifested themselves.

Some parents offer cash bribes to their children if they don't smoke until the age of eighteen. This sometimes works, but a better approach is to point out the dangers of dependency and how this interferes with free will. A parent can say something like: 'Clearly, I can't stop you smoking if you really want to, but before becoming addicted, ask yourself whether you really want to be dependent on something like nicotine.' You can then point out just how very addictive cigarettes are, and that the reason why most people don't give up is because they imagine they can't.

Parents should understand that addictions always start when the individual feels empty inside, and as if he or she has no real place in the world. Any teenager who has started smoking heavily is probably unhappy, which is why so many adolescents in children's homes smoke. The concerned parent will try to find out the cause of the unhappiness, and see if it can be reversed, rather than simply condemning the smoking habit.

9.

FOOD AND OTHER ADDICTIONS

Of course, it is possible to become addicted to just about anything — or anybody. Mostly, addictions to such artefacts as computers, old films, work, Mars bars or roasted peanuts, do not constitute a serious life crisis, and are merely different aspects of the personality manifesting themselves. We may say that a certain person is 'addicted' to sailing or windsurfing, meaning that he lives for the weekend when indulgence in the favourite sport will be possible. The only time to worry, with any addiction, is when it is adversely affecting life, health and relationships, and when one's whole existence is completely dominated by the wish to satisfy a craving.

It is rare that a hobby such as reading romantic novels, computer programming, or stamp collecting, would come into this category; but any dedicated hobbyist should ensure that the activity is not being pursued as an escape route from having satisfying relationships with other people and the outside world. If this was the case, then a life crisis would certainly loom. There is always potential danger when a hobby becomes the most important aspect of anybody's life. A person who shuns normal interaction with other people in order to pursue a hobby single-mindedly should ask — what am I trying to escape from, and why? There may be no simple answers, but even just asking the questions will help to put the hobby into greater perspective.

Food Addiction
Food, however, is different. Unlike most other potentially addictive substances and activities we can't choose to ignore food. We all have to eat. Most of us, too, enjoy eating. Food constitutes one of our earliest sensual gratifications and remains a pleasure throughout life. It is a potent symbol of love and affection. When

we like somebody, or wish to get to know them better, we invite them out to lunch or home to dinner. Many business deals are concluded over the business lunch, and many a seduction routine starts off with a candlelit dinner. Virtually any celebration includes food, and much time and trouble is spent in preparing wonderful dishes.

The great majority of people — at least, those for whom the actual obtaining of food is not a problem — don't think all that much about eating. We wish to satisfy hunger, of course, and will look forward to a good meal, but we would not say that our lives are dominated by food, to the exclusion of all else.

But there are people, mainly women, who are so very obsessed with food that they can think of nothing else. These are the yo-yo dieters, who are starving one minute and stuffing themselves the next. There is a name for this compulsion — bulimia nervosa — and it can be as dangerous and life-destroying an addiction as alcohol or heroin. Bulimia is a condition which definitely requires outside, professional help, as it is a progressive illness which has very little to do with actual greed.

Paulette Maisner, herself a former bulimic, now runs a Centre for Eating Disorders in Brighton. She feels that the condition can be very serious, is detrimental to health and happiness, and that it is far more common than is usually thought. As with other addictive forms of behaviour, bulimia carries in its wake great devastation of personality and lifestyle.

Paulette feels that bulimia first sets in when women diet too much and take in too few calories over a long period of time, so that their bodies are eventually crying out for nourishment. After a time, the mind/body links become confused, as with other addictive forms of behaviour, and the woman can no longer tell whether she is hungry or not.

Bulimia, Paulette says, very often begins with stress and a feeling of inner emptiness. Victims may lack self-assertiveness, and have very low self-esteem, which are exactly the personality triggers for other addictions setting in. Future bulimics may also feel lonely, bored and frustrated. The definition of a bulimic is somebody who spends all day starving, or eating the absolute minimum, then goes home and stuffs everything in sight, including cereal straight from the packet, raw meat, dog and cat food even. There is no longer any link between hunger and satisfaction. In fact, the more a bulimic eats the hungrier she feels; and the food she stuffs in this crazy way is probably not even nutritious. At the end of the ghastly feast, when the bulimic will have consumed anything from between 7,000 and 13,000 calories, she will attempt to purge or vomit up the excess food. In time, this chaotic pattern of eating brings about actual ill health and also a kind of mental disorder. A bulimic is a true addict, unable to function in a normal way any more.

Dr Peter Slade, a clinical psychologist at Liverpool University, is undertaking the first really scientific research into the problems of overeating and bulimia. His view is that eating patterns can become a dreadful addiction, as people get hooked and then find they cannot reverse the destructive pattern of behaviour they themselves have constructed. His belief is that bulimia is a way of life that modern women in western society are attempting in order to cope with deep-seated emotional problems.

Overcoming bulimia

Bulimia, or binge eating, causes terrible guilt and anxiety and it is an addiction that is not easy to cure. It is possible to have the condition treated on an out-patient basis in hospital, and Dr Hubert Lacey, of St George's Hospital, London, has reported a certain amount of success with bulimics. Patients are treated in groups of five, and therapy involves keeping a diary, setting up a contract with the therapist, and several sessions of psychotherapy.

Self-help measures include keeping a detailed eating diary, and, before starting to eat compulsively, making a phone call. This simple act can be an all-important step in breaking the compulsion. Paulette Maisner says: 'Making a phone call, which takes up your entire attention for a few minutes, gives you valuable human contact as well as turning your attention to something else. When you come off the phone, you will find that the urge to binge has receded.'

Another valuable self-help measure is to take up a hobby which can be pursued when the urge to binge is uppermost. Paulette Maisner herself started making stained glass windows with this in mind; she has now become so expert that she has reached professional ability and is receiving commissions. She says: 'I would cut one piece of glass before starting to eat, and I found this helped a lot.' The hobby could be anything which is capable both of absorbing one's entire attention for a few minutes, and which can be taken up without complicated equipment being set up first. Jigsaw or crossword puzzles, knitting or embroidery, or pottery, are all hobbies that work in this way. Anything that can completely occupy your hands and brains for a time, and which you can do on your own, can break the link with food, and can help you to forget about bingeing until the urge recedes.

Addiction to Violence

Another type of addiction, not mentioned so far but which can be very dangerous indeed, is an addiction to violence. I'm not talking here about those whose own behaviour is violent, but people who form relationships with violent individuals. These are mainly 'battered women', and it is not always realized how potent such an addiction can be. The obvious reaction is to feel sorry for women who are on the receiving end of terrible violence, but not everybody realizes that many women may actually be addicted to this and may act in such ways that they keep bringing it about.

An addiction to violence is exactly the same as any other addiction. It starts off when the individual, usually a woman, feels very low in self-esteem and self-confidence. She may also be habituated to violence by coming from a violent background, and unable to break the link with this destructive behaviour. Commonly, women who marry violent men come from backgrounds where physical blows were an aspect of everyday life. As we have seen, children learn by example rather than anything else and a girl who grows up in a violent home may regard such behaviour as normal. This means that she, consciously or unconsciously, seeks out a mate who will be violent to her.

It must be stressed that battered women do not, of course, want to have their ribs smashed or their faces beaten to a pulp. But time and again women who are addicted to violence will marry, or form relationships with, men who are violent. Also, they will tend to go back time and again to the same violent man, no matter what injuries he may have inflicted in the past.

In her book *Prone to Violence*, former battered wives' champion Erin Pizzey, now writing about violence in fictional form in her novels, explains how certain women can become addicted to violence, so that they continually seek it out and provoke it. Whether you are on the giving or the receiving end of violence, adrenalin is stimulated, and can temporarily provide a shot of excitement into a life that may otherwise be humdrum and tedious. It is possible to become addicted to this kind of stimulation, believes Erin Pizzey, which is not really all that different from an addiction to gambling or fast driving.

Anybody who recognizes that they may be actually addicted to violence, or who is aware that relationships are continually being formed with violent partners, should get in touch with the nearest branch of Women's Aid to seek expert help. Destructive patterns can usually be broken only with the help and support of others, as it is not always easy to realize how deeply the addiction may be embedded in the personality.

It is always tempting, for those not themselves addicted, to take the attitude that people should 'snap out' of negative forms of behaviour; but it is hard for non-addicts to understand how deeply habits may become ingrained. Anybody who is in the position of an onlooker, and who cannot see why the destructive behaviour continues, should try reversing some of their own habits, such as getting up in the morning in a different order. Even trying to change something as apparently insignificant as this is difficult enough. How much more difficult then to change a form of behaviour that has been established and which has set in over many years.

Bad habits, such as over-eating, gambling, and drug taking, can be broken, but only when the individual has a strong and positive attitude to overcome the problem that may be wrecking several lives. Very often an addiction will not be tackled until the addict's life is in such a mess that some form of action becomes imperative.

All addicts should realize that they do not have to face the problem alone. There are now many help organizations, from self-help societies to professional bodies, which have recognized the power of addictions and the problems involved in breaking them.

Last Word
Nobody should underestimate the problems involved in breaking an addiction. Conversely, nobody should ever feel that the addiction has become so strongly ingrained that it is impossible to reverse it. However bad it may seem, any addiction can be overcome where there is strong motivation. But unless the motivation is there, the addiction will remain.

It should not be assumed that every addict wants to become better, or that life will automatically be improved as a result of help and treatment. There are those — fortunately a minority — who are determined to embark on a course of self-destruction; and when this is the case, very little help can be given.

But such voluntary self-destruction applies to very few people indeed. Most addicts are people who are simply not aware that their habit has taken hold to such a great extent. In many cases, the extent of the addiction is not realized until an attempt is made to break the habit. It is only then that the person is conscious of how many hours in the day, how many thoughts, are occupied with satisfying the craving. By their very nature, cravings never can be satisfied — because every fix serves to deepen the habit. There is no possible way of satisfying a gambling compulsion, no way that an alcoholic can ever get enough to drink. There is just not enough money, not enough drink, not enough food in the world to satisfy the true addict, and someone who is physically addicted simply cannot function without the desired substance.

It is only when the craving itself can be abolished that the habit will start to have a less vice-like hold. But this can only happen when the addict perceives that there is something better out there — that life has more to offer than the attempt to satisfy the addiction. This is why those working with addicts must stress the importance not simply of giving up the addiction, but of putting something better in its place.

This is why successful help agencies such as ACCEPT understand the value of interesting hobbies and activities which can be viewed, not just as a way of passing the time, but as useful in their own right. To help any addict, attention has to be diverted from the drug or activity towards more positive and rewarding forms of behaviour.

It is undoubtedly worth persisting, as any former addict will testify. All those who have managed to break a bad or destructive addiction know that life can be immeasurably improved afterwards. Once the link with addictive behaviour is broken, self-esteem, self-confidence and true assertiveness is regained. Life is then not only incomparably better for the addict, but for all those who come into contact. So in helping an addict, people are also helping themselves.

USEFUL ADDRESSES

DRUGS
The following is a list of drug agencies, clinics and rehabilitation houses. It is by no means exhaustive, as new treatment centres and facilities are coming into being all the time.

Advice Centres and Information
Addiction Research Unit, Institute of Psychiatry, 101 Denmark Hill, Southwark, London SE5 8AF. (For professionals only.)
Association of Independent Doctors against Addiction: 13 Devonshire Place, London W1.
Birmingham Drugline: Dale House, New Meeting Street, Birmingham B4 7SX. Tel: 021-632 6364.
Blenheim Friends: Tel: 01-960 5590 and 01-328 6556.
Churches Council on Alcohol and Drugs: 4 Southampton Row, London WC1B 4AA.
Drug Treatment Centre: 53 Basement, Vincent Square, London SW1. (Help and Advice for young people.)
Hungerford Drug Project: 26 Craven Street, London WC2. Tel: 01-930 4688.
Institute for Drug Dependence: 1-4 Hatton Place, Hatton Garden, London EC1 8ND.
Lifeline Project: A Manchester-based agency. Joddrell Street, Manchester M3 3HE. Tel: 061-832 6353.
Merseyside Drugs Council: Tel: 051-709 0074.
Release: 1 Elgin Avenue, London W9. Tel: 01-603 8654 (24-hour emergency service). During office hours: 01-289 1123. Advice on all types of drug misuse. Release has many leaflets on drug misuse and how to deal with it. This agency also gives valuable advice on the legal situation.
SCODA: Standing Conference on Drug Abuse, Kingsbury House,

3 Blackburn Road, London NW6 1XA. Tel: 01-328 6556.
(Information on most drug agencies and help centres
throughout the UK and, like Release, they will also give
information on the legal penalties for drug misuse.
Turning Point: Cap House, 9/12 Long Lane, London EC1A 9HA.
Tel: 01-606 3947. Advice on all aspects of drug use. This agency
can put users and their relatives in touch with agencies and
centres giving specific types of help. They are in touch with
most of the rehabilitation houses and street agencies in the
country, also hospital clinics.

Women Only

D.A.W.N. (Drugs, Alcohol, Women, Nationally): 146 Queen
Victoria Street, London EC4 4BX. Tel: 01-236 8125. Leaflets and
information.

ALCOHOL

ACCEPT (Addictions Community Centres for Education,
Prevention and Treatment): 200 Seagrave Road, London W6.
Tel: 01-385 2481.
Action on Alcohol Abuse: 26 Craven Street, London WC2 5NT.
Tel: 01-837 7344/5.
Al-anon Family Groups: 61 Dover Street, London SE1 4YF.
Alcoholics Anonymous: P.O. Box 514, 11 Redcliffe Gardens,
London SW10 9BQ. Tel: 01-352 9779.
Alcoholics Anonymous: London Regional Telephone Service,
London SW1. Tel: 01-834 8202.
Alcoholics Recovery Project: 6 Kings Cross Road, London WC1.
Tel: 01-837 2686.
(Regional Branches of Alcoholics Anonymous, Al-Anon for
Relatives and Alcoholics Recovery Projects can be found in
the telephone book)
The Broadway Clinic: Wealdstone, Harrow. Tel: 01-427 7700.
Drinkwatchers: Information from 200 Seagrave Road, London
W6.
Greater London Alcohol Advisory Service: 146 Queen Victoria
Street, London EC4. Tel: 01-248 8406.
Medical Council on Alcoholism: 3 Grosvenor Crescent, London
SW1X 7EE.

Residential Centres and Rehabilitation Houses

Blenheim Project: 7 Thorpe Close, London W10. Tel: 01-960 5599.

(Long term rehabilitation.) Also several good leaflets available on aspects of drug misuse.

Broadway Lodge: Weston-super-Mare. Tel: 0934 812319 (Private.)

Cheadle Royal Hospital: Cheshire. Tel: 061-428 9511. (Private.)

City Roads: 385 City Road, London EC1. Tel: 01-278 8671/8672 (Short stay rehabilitation: 3 weeks.)

Phoenix House: Tel: 01-699 5748. (Long term rehabilitation.)

The Priory: Roehampton, London SW13. Tel: 01-876 8261. (Private.)

The Retreat: York. Tel: 0904 412551. (Private.)

Roma: 65/67 Talgarth Road, Hammersmith, London W14. Tel: 01-603 8383. (For notified users only.)

Suffolk House: Longbridge, Slough Road, Iver Heath, Bucks SL0 0EB. Tel: 0895-56449. (Long-term rehabilitation.)

Self-Help Associations

Families Anonymous: 88 Caledonian Road, London N1. Tel: 01-278 8805. (For relatives and friends of users.)

Narcotics Anonymous: London: Tel: 01-351 6794/6066/6067. Bristol: Tel: 0272 40084. Dublin: P.O. Box 1368, Sheriff Street, Dublin 1. Self-help organization for drug users.

GAMBLING

Gamblers Anonymous: 17/23 Blantyre Street, London SW10. Tel: 01-352 3060. Information also on Gam-Anon Family Groups and Young GA.

National Council on Gambling: 26 Bedford Square, London WC1B 3HU.

TRANQUILLIZERS

Release: 1 Elgin Avenue, London W9. Release has leaflets on tranquillizer withdrawal and lists of self-help groups.

Tranx: 17 Peel Road, Harrow, Middlesex HA3 7QX.

Tranx Release: Anita Gordon, 14 Moorfield Square, Southfields, Northampton NN3 5BD.

SMOKING

ASH: (Action on Smoking and Health): 5/11 Mortimer Street, London W1N 7RH. Tel: 01-637 9843. Free information on how to give up smoking is available and they also have a list of clinics, both private and NHS.

Association of Hypnotists and Psychotherapists: Blythe Tutorial

College, Nelson, Lancs. Tel: 0282-699378. This college has a register of practitioners.

British Anti-Smoking Education Society: 78 Langley Road, Watford, Herts WD1 3PL.

British Society of Dental and Medical Hypnosis: 42 Links Road, Ashtead, Surrey KT21 2HJ. Tel: 03722 73522. This society has a list of members in various parts of the country, but referral from a doctor is needed.

National Society of Non-Smokers: Latimer House, London W1P 7DE.

FOOD

The Maisner Centre for Eating Disorders: 41 Preston Street, Brighton, East Sussex. Tel: 0273 729818.

VIOLENCE

National Women's Aid Federation: 374 Grays Inn Road, London WC1. Tel: 01-580 7928.

FURTHER READING

John Marks *The Benzodiazepines: Use, Overuse, Misuse* (MTP Press, 1978).

Mary Manning *The Drugs Menace* (Columbus, 1985).

Drugs: What Every Parent Should Know Free from the Institute for Drug Dependence (see Drugs—Advice Centres and Information, Useful Addresses section).

Paulette Maisner and Jenny Pulling *Feasting and Fasting* (Fontana, 1985).

Paulette Maisner *The Food Trap* (George Allen and Unwin, 1985).

John Nicholson *Habits: Why You Do What You Do* (Pan, 1977).

Royal College of Physicians *Health or Smoking?* (Pitman, 1983).

W. R. Miller and R. F. Munoz *How To Control Your Drinking* (Sheldon Press, 1983).

Barbara Gordon *I'm Dancing as Fast as I can* (Hamish Hamilton, 1980).

Bobbie Jacobson *The Ladykillers: Why Smoking is a Feminist Issue* (Pluto Press, 1982).

Richard Mackarness *A Little of What You Fancy: How To Control Smoking and Other Cravings* (Fontana, 1985).

Helen Bethune *Off The Hook — Coping with Addiction* (Methuen, 1985).

Erin Pizzey *Prone To Violence* (Hamlyn, 1982).

Ray Hodgson and Peter Miller *Self-Watching: Addictions, Habits, Compulsions — What To Do About Them* (Century, 1982).

Peter Honey *Solving Your Personal Problems* (Sheldon Press, 1983).

Joy Melville *The Tranquilliser Trap* (Fontana, 1984).

INDEX

Seconal, 44
'sex drug', the, 41
Sherlock, Professor Dame
    Sheila, 85
Simpson, David, 120
Slade, Dr Peter, 130
smoking, 11,12,13,14,116-127,
    health risks of, 121-122
    giving up, 123-4
    treatment clinics, 125
    what parents can do, 126-7
    who smokes and why,
        119-121
Soho Project, 94
soap operas, 15
solvents, 14,44-7
'speed', 26,61
St George's Hospital, 130
Standard, The, 61
Standing Conference on
    Drug Abuse (SCODA),
    92
Sternbach, Dr Leo, 104
street agencies, 68-9
stress, 14
Suffolk House, 71-3
sugar addiction, 15

teenagers, 25,26-7
    and alcohol, 84-6
    and drugs, 51-3
    and smoking, 119-20
temazepam, 104
tetrahydrocannibol, 37
tobacco, 55 See also
    smoking, nicotine
Townsend, Peter, 23

tranquillizers, 12,14,15,62,
    103-15
    coming off, 113-5
    how they work, 104-5
    withdrawal symptoms,
        105-8
Tranquillizer Trap, The, 107
Tranx Release, 108-9, 110,
    113-4
toluene, 46
Triads, 24,29
Triazolam, 107
Tuinal, 44
Turning Point, 71-2

Valium, 89, 104, 106, 108-9
    110-11
Vetter Charles, 83,89
Vietnam war, the, 42
violence, 131-2
vitamin deficiency (from
    alcohol), 81,92
vomiting, 58

What Everybody Should
    Know About Drugs, 48
Which?, 81
withdrawal at home (from
    heroin) 76
withdrawal symptoms, 17,
    103, 105-6
women and heroin, 53
Women's Aid, 132
workaholism, 15
World Health Organization,
    120

yoga, 88, 112